group production
organization
and technology

# group production organization and technology

### E. K. IVANOV

*English translation by E. Bishop, B.Sc.(Tech.)*

*Technical adviser and editor: T. J. Grayson*

Leverhulme Research Fellow in Soviet Engineering
Production, The University of Birmingham

London
BUSINESS PUBLICATIONS LIMITED

This work was first published in the U.S.S.R. in 1963 under the title of
*Organizatsiya I. Tekhnologiya Gruppovogo Proizvodstva,*
*Edited by Professor G. A. Glazor*
First published in the English language, 1968, by Business Publications
Limited. English language translation copyright © Business Publi-
cations Limited, 1968

A *Light Production Engineering* Book

This book has been set in 10 on 13 pt Plantin by Cox and Wyman
Limited, Fakenham, for the publishers, Business Publications Limited
(registered office: 180 Fleet Street, London, E.C.4), publishing
offices: Mercury House, Waterloo Road, London, S.E.1

MADE AND PRINTED IN GREAT BRITAIN

# contents

*List of Illustrations*                                                          vii

*Foreword by T. J. Grayson*                                                       ix

*Preface*                                                                         xi

1   A BRIEF OUTLINE OF GROUP TECHNOLOGY                                            1

2   THE CLASSIFICATION OF COMPONENTS                                              4

3   THE COMPOSITE PART                                                            8

4   THE ORGANIZATION OF SMALL- AND MEDIUM-BATCH PRODUCTION
    ON THE BASIS OF LARGE-BATCH AND MASS-PRODUCTION PRINCIPLES                    12

5   THE USE OF GROUP TECHNIQUES IN MACHINING COMPONENTS ON
    CAPSTAN LATHES, CENTRE LATHES AND MILLING MACHINES                            16

6   THE GROUP TECHNOLOGY SECTION                                                  33

7   THE USE OF GROUP TECHNIQUES IN THE MANUFACTURE OF PRESSURE
    DIECASTINGS AND LIQUID-METAL STAMPINGS                                        38

8   THE USE OF GROUP TECHNOLOGY IN FINISHING, ASSEMBLING AND
    OTHER PRODUCTION PROCESSES                                                    48

9   GROUP TOOLING                                                                 56

10  THE MODIFICATION OF EQUIPMENT IN GROUP PRODUCTION CON-
    DITIONS                                                                       61

11  PROGRAMME-CONTROLLED MACHINE TOOLS                                            64

12  THE GROUP TECHNOLOGY SHOP                                                     69

13  THE ORGANIZATION OF LABOUR PLANNING AND RATE-FIXING IN
    GROUP PRODUCTION CONDITIONS                                                   75

**14** THE PROVISION OF SUPPLIES FOR GROUP PRODUCTION 87

**15** THE FUNCTION OF THE CHIEF DESIGNER'S AND CHIEF PRODUCTION ENGINEER'S DEPARTMENTS IN GROUP PRODUCTION CONDITIONS 101

**16** THE COST EFFECTIVENESS OF GROUP PRODUCTION 107

**17** THE PREPARATION OF A PLANT FOR CHANGING OVER TO GROUP TECHNOLOGY 110

**18** THE ROLE OF THE TRADE UNIONS AND THE PARTY ORGANIZATIONS IN THE ASSIMILATION OF GROUP PRODUCTION TECHNIQUES 117

**19** THE DEVELOPMENT OF GROUP TECHNOLOGY 122

*Index* 127

# list of illustrations

1.1 A range of components to be machined           *facing page*    4

1.2 The same components arranged in groups       *facing page*    5

2.1 General scheme of component classification                   4

2.2 Component classification on the basis of geometric shape    5

2.3 Component classification on the basis of design and operations    6

2.4 Component classification on the basis of similarities in the equipment, tooling and settings used    6

3.1 A method of arriving at the composite part    9

3.2 Setting up a capstan lathe to make the composite part    10

5.1 A group of simple components machined on capstan lathes    19

5.2 A group of more complicated components machined on capstan lathes    20

5.3 Another group of complicated components machined on capstan lathes    20

5.4 A centre lathe fitted with a turret-head       *facing page*    5

5.5 A group of shaft-type components for group machining on centre lathes    22

5.6 A group of complicated bushes for group machining on centre lathes    23

5.7 A group of components for group machining (slotted) on millers    24

5.8 Another group of components for group milling    25

5.9 A group of components requiring the same group machining sequence    25

5.10 Capstan lathe setup for group machining    32

6.1 A collet chuck for holding piece blanks of large components    35

6.2 A slotting head for capstan lathes       *facing page*    20

6.3 A copy slide for cutting pairs of threads       *facing page*    20

6.4 A work cabinet for storing tools       *facing page*    20

7.1 A group die block for use in pressure diecasting machines       *facing page*    21

7.2 A group die block with cassette-type inserts       *facing page*    52

7.3 Metal pouring setup for liquid-metal stamping    43

7.4 Liquid-metal stamping with extrusion and solidification under pressure    44

7.5 Liquid-metal stamping without extrusion    44

8.1 A magnetic clamping attachment for chromium-plating 51

8.2 A group of objectives suitable for assembly on a group basis 53

9.1 A group lathe chuck *facing page* 52

9.2 A group jig with interchangeable strips *facing page* 53

9.3 A group milling attachment *facing page* 53

9.4 A group jig *facing page* 68

9.5 A lathe group attachment 60

10.1 A centre lathe fitted with a hydraulic copy slide *facing page* 68

10.2 A special unit-head machine for milling shaped slots *facing page* 69

11.1 Capstan lathes fitted with programme controllers *facing page* 69

12.1 An attachment for continuous milling 72

12.2 Graph showing the increase in labour productivity in the machine shop 74

12.3 Graph showing the reduction in machining labour costs in the machine shop 74

12.4 Graph showing the increase in output from the machine shop 74

13.1 Comparative diagram showing the current rates and those established by the group method 86

13.2 Nomogram for milling times using cutter heads, as a function of the length and width of the surface 86

15.1 Graph showing the reduction in technical documentation 103

15.2 Graph showing the increasing assimilation of different group production operations 105

15.3 Graph of the organization of production preparation in connection with the introduction of group technology 105

# foreword

by T. J. Grayson

THE PRESENT work, translated from the Russian, is the first in a series on group technology and its applications. It is intended for a wide audience of engineers and managers and assumes that the reader has no detailed knowledge of the subject.

Group technology has been employed for some 20 years in the USSR, and this work examines briefly the developments during this period. Ivanov discusses the principles laid down by S. P. Mitrofanov and also examines the application of the group method in other areas of manufacture in the factory.

The principles outlined in this work are in the main sufficient to answer all the questions that the reader is likely to pose about the introduction of the group method in factories, but there are three points which need elaborating.

The classification scheme employed in this work is a production system designed to bring together those components similar in shape and manufactured on similar pieces of equipment. It does not, however, assist in the other interests of sections of the factory. It does not, for instance, supply a common part numbering system; it does not directly assist in the standardization of components etc. If the reader's interests are purely on the production side then the present system will suffice. However, if the wider concept is required then a code of the Brisch Polycode form is required.

The other problem and one which although mentioned briefly in this work cannot be overstressed, is the problem of human relationships. Before group technology can be introduced into a factory every employee should be aware of the implications and operating criteria of this form of production. This is especially important in the relationships existing between the designer and the production engineer, for it is sometimes necessary to redesign parts to comply with the requirements of the group. Each person must understand his colleagues' particular problems. One leading Soviet engineer is reported as saying that the development of the group method depends on the best possible human relationships in the factory and an awareness of the fundamental aims of this manufacturing technique.

There is also a word of warning which must be given. Group technology should be introduced into a factory only after the management is sure that the production control system they propose to use with the method is adequate. In a number of instances disastrous effects have occurred in Soviet factories using group technology without working out the details of the production control system. As there is no universal control system to suit all requirements, then the system outlined in the text will have to be redrafted to meet the would-be user's particular requirements.

The text has been carefully checked to ensure that the translation is correct in substance and that no Soviet phraseology has been used. The only part of this work which refers to an aspect which will not be relevant to the Western firm is that section which deals with the role of the party organizations within the factory. I shall not attempt to examine this question in this foreword, but suggest that if any reader is particularly interested in this question he turns to David Granick's book *The Red Executive* (published by Macmillan and Co. Ltd, 1960).

Finally, I wish to acknowledge the financial assistance I have received from the Leverhulme Trust, and the material and intellectual assistance from my colleagues in the Department of Engineering Production and the Centre for Russian and East European Studies at the University of Birmingham.

*January 1968*

T. J. GRAYSON,
Leverhulme Research Fellow
in Soviet Engineering
Production,
University of Birmingham.

# preface

THE FAR-REACHING tasks set before Soviet industry by the XXIInd CPSU*
Congress, in respect of increased labour productivity and lower production
costs, will necessitate the large-scale adoption of new, more progressive
working methods and will entail a search for novel ways of organizing
production. The latter must provide for making full use of every means of
production, including the introduction of the latest processes and progressive techniques.

The adoption of new processes and more progressive techniques
invariably and inevitably involves a major programme of production
planning work. The volume of technological documentation in circula-
ion in the engineering and instrument-making plants is generally enormous, far exceeding the volume of drawing-office documentation. Detailed
step-by-step instructions are drawn up for the majority of components,
many of which specify the use of complicated special attachments
that must usually be scrapped when the components for a new product
are made.

As a result, little use is made in small- and medium-batch production of
such progressive production processes as pressure diecasting, cold forming
and the use of plastics, on the ground that the costs associated with production planning cannot be recovered from the limited volume of saleable
output. Again, little use is made of such production equipment as capstan
lathes and automatics, and the final assembly operations are mostly carried
out on a one-off basis.

The overall result is that the engineering and instrument-making plants
will be compelled to seek new approaches and different methods of organizing production if they are to achieve a situation in which small- and
medium-batch production can be organized and planned on the lines
familiar to the mass-production and large-batch enterprises.

One method of solving this problem is the group machining method

* CPSU. Communist Party of the Soviet Union.

developed by Doctor S. P. Mitrofanov, which is already in use in a number of factories in the Soviet Union and other countries.

The group machining method constitutes a novel scientific approach to the planning of component-machining techniques.

Practical experience in the plants of the Leningrad Optical-Mechanical Association has shown that group techniques can be applied to component machining on capstans, lathes, drilling machines, pressure diecasting, liquid-metal stamping, finishing operations and so on; that it widens the scope for reducing the time and cost of production planning, makes for simpler production organization and control, and increases labour productivity by 25–40 per cent.

The group method is based on the classification of components by sub-division, in the last resort, into groups for which group production sequences can be developed.

The development of group production sequences gives rise to group operations, and it is possible to make each machine tool (or station) highly specialized to handle the group of components allocated to it. In other words, the machine tools are specialized and the stage is set for the large-scale adoption in medium- and small-batch production of the organizational forms and methods appropriate to large-batch and mass production.

The author's purpose in writing this book is to present an account of the principles of organizing production on the group basis in terms that the reader with no prior knowledge of the subject can understand, and to demonstrate by practical examples how to make a start on the development of group techniques and how to undertake planning, rate-fixing and the supply of materials and services. The scope also includes the problems of designing and using group attachments, the change-over from single-component to group attachments and the recommended detailed designs for specific group attachments.

Examples are quoted to illustrate the problems of scheduling and the allocation of machines and operators to given components, since these are the critical problems in the change-over to group technology.

E.K.I.

# I

# a brief outline
# of group technology

IN SMALL- and even medium-batch production conditions the component batch sizes are usually small, and it is impossible to maintain a constant load of components of a given type on the machine tools for any length of time. Consequently, little use can be made of progressive machining techniques and there is insufficient scope for the adoption of high-productivity equipment such as capstans and automatics. The machines inevitably stand idle every time a change is made from one component to another, and these interruptions complicate production organization and planning and much time is lost.

The current method of working out separate production sequences for every single component required in batch production is not conducive to the reduction of interruptions in the operation of the machine tools. This situation arises from the fact that the production sequences are usually drawn up in the light of past experience supported by the specific information at the production engineer's disposal. Also, the current methods of organizing production planning for a wide range of different components frequently make no provision for the full utilization of past experience in the drawing up of production sequences and the design of suitable tooling.

The result is that completely different sequences are frequently laid down for identical or closely similar components against all reason, and they must then be followed up by the issue of a large volume of production documentation and the spending of large amounts of time and money in designing and making the attachments and tools.

It is not by chance, therefore, that the component production sequences adopted in batch production plants are characterized by the use of fewer special tooling setups than in mass-production plants, and that little if any use at all is made of pneumatic, hydraulic and other high-productivity attachments.

One fundamental step capable of bringing mass-production principles within reach of small- and medium-batch enterprises is the adoption of the component group machining approach.

The basic concept of component group machining is that instead of the production sequences, tooling and machine setups being based on single components, the planning unit becomes an entire group of similar components or operations calling for the use of similar equipment and tooling.

The following example will prove instructive. To draw up separate production sequences for all of the components shown in Fig. 1.1, (facing page 4) one would have to prepare a detailed job card for each one and then design and make the individual attachments. The number of job cards must equal the number of different components; the number of attachments will depend on the proportionate use made of attachments. Production planning on these lines is a protracted and expensive business, and the costs will not always be recovered if the batch sizes are small; hence the production costs will be appreciably increased.

The group system completely alters the situation. Fig. 1.2 (facing page 5) shows the several hundred components arranged systematically in 20 groups, for which only 20 group production sequences and group attachments need be considered.

Thus, the following advantages are achieved simultaneously.

1 The volume of production documentation and number of attachments are reduced.
2 A significant proportion of any new components can be allocated to existing groups for machining on the machines and with the attachments set up for that group.
3 It becomes possible to use a wide range of high-productivity equipment and unit-head machine tools, and to adapt the existing equipment specifically to the group operations allocated to them.
4 The stage is set for the adoption of group flowlines as the most advanced method of organizing production.

Once the entire range of components has been classified (allocated to the groups), production planning consists of the following stages.

1 The drawing up of group production sequences, including instructions on setting up for the composite part and the group attachments required; if the group sequence and attachment reflect previous developments no new planning work is required.
2 The drawing up of component production sequences.
3 The design of any group or single-component attachments for which previously designed attachments cannot be adapted.
4 The manufacture of the attachments.
5 A check on the group settings and operations, carried out by machining a few components from each group using the group attachments and tooling.
6 The correction as necessary of the production sequences and attachments.
7 The issue of an order to introduce the group process or tooling.
8 The drawing up of job rates and their adoption in the machine shop.

The group approach offers a radical solution to the problem of eliminating unjustified variety in the range of operations used; the selected operations can be raised to the technical level of those adopted in large-batch and mass production by the use of high-productivity quick-setting attachments and tooling. The stage is set for the effective modernization and automation of the production equipment.

# 2

# the classification
# of components

THE GROUP production sequences are drawn up on the basis of a prior classification and grouping of the components machined in the plant or shop concerned. The system and method of classification must be practical, and geared to the specific needs of the enterprise.

The component classification adopted in the Optical-Mechanical Association plants (Fig. 2.1) was based on the principle of allocating each component to the equipment best fitted for machining it. This gave

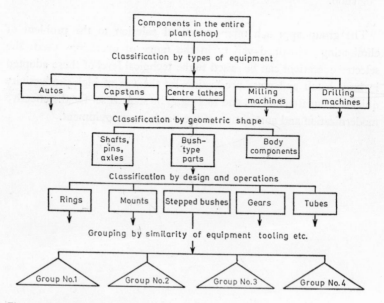

*Fig. 2.1* General scheme of component classification

*Fig. 1.1* A range of components to be machined

Fig. *1.2* The same components arranged in groups

Fig. *5.4* A centre lathe fitted with a turret-head

rise to component classes machined on automatics, capstans, ordinary lathes, millers, drilling, and grinding and other machines, as the first stage in grouping.

The components within each class were then subdivided in accordance with their most characteristic features, namely:

*Geometric shape,* defined as the set of geometrical elements making up the outline of the component. The lathe class, for example (Fig. 2.2), was subdivided into shaft-type components (shafts, pins, axles, etc.), bush-type components and body components. This constituted the second stage of the grouping.

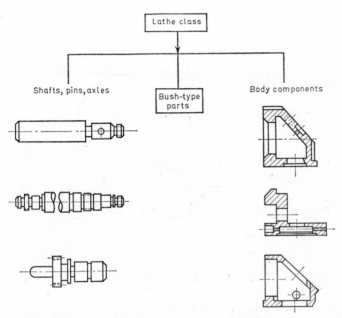

*Fig. 2.2* Component classification on the basis of geometric shape

*Design and operations,* defined as the set of surfaces requiring machining. The bush-type components in the lathe class, for example (Fig. 2.3), were now subdivided into rings, mountings, multi-step bushes, gears, tubes and so on. This constituted the third stage of the grouping.

*Similarity of production sequence,* in the light of the component dimensions, attachments and tooling used, equipment required and settings.

B

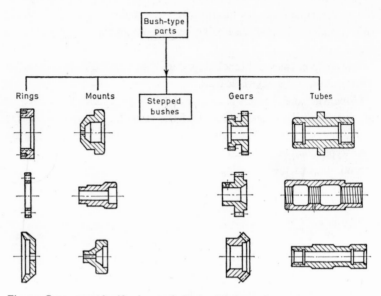

*Fig. 2.3* Component classification on the basis of design and operations

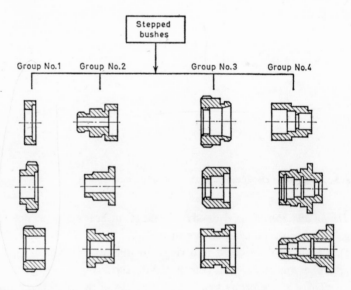

*Fig. 2.4* Component classification on the basis of similarities in the equipment, tooling and settings used

For example, the stepped bushes within the lathe class were subdivided into four component groups (Fig. 2.4). This constituted the fourth and last stage in the present component grouping system.

The component groups arrived at after the final subdivision are the important end-product of the exercise. They represent the fundamental technological units around which the group production sequences and tooling are designed. The larger groupings into classes and so on, through the various stages of classification, facilitate the final subdivision and are merely intermediate aids.

The number of stages, the criteria for each stage and the order of classification as a whole must be adapted to the specific conditions obtaining within the enterprise concerned.

The components can be grouped on the basis of the entire production sequence, taken as a unified entity from start to finish, or on the basis of one or more intermediate operations or sets of operations.

It will be clear from the examples just described how the preparatory work should be carried out within the plant. On the other hand, it must be pointed out that this particular approach is offered as no more than an example; modifications of one sort or another may be required in each specific case, depending upon the nature of the product.

# 3

# the composite part

WHEN ALL of the components in production have been classified into machining groups, the next step is to develop the group production sequences and to design the group attachments.

However, before launching into an account of the methods of drawing up production sequences and organizing group production, something must be said on the subject of *the composite part*.

Roughly speaking, the composite part represents the most complicated component within the group, made up as are all of the others of a set of simple geometrical elements (surfaces). For instance, components turned on lathes may include cylindrical and conical internal and external surfaces, endfaces, various recesses, knurled surfaces, threads and so on; prismatic components may include various faces, holes, grooves and so on.

By combining the common geometrical elements and dimensions in different ways, one can obtain a very wide variety of different components. Each represents a special case of the composite part, possibly simpler in shape and different in dimensions but nevertheless featuring fundamentally the same elements as the composite part. The composite part does not always exist as such; in fact in the majority of cases it must be arrived at by synthesis.

Having examined all of the drawings for the group concerned, the production engineer selects from the set of similar components the one made up of the various elements in the most typical way.

This component is taken as the basis of the intended group, and a separate drawing is made of it. The remaining drawings are next re-examined to select further components that differ from the first by the presence of other shape-determining geometrical elements. These elements are transferred to the new drawing of the basic component. In this way a generalized composite part that includes all of the elements found in any component within the group is arrived at.

Fig. 3.1 illustrates the method of arriving at the composite part.

By adding gradually to the complexity of the characteristic component in this manner it is possible to extend and finally determine the range of components one can include within the machining group.

The nature of the rough component and the equipment to be used, the machining sequence, the tooling and the setting for the composite

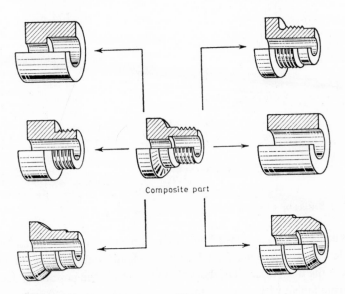

Composite part

*Fig. 3.1* A method of arriving at the composite part

part thus determine the entire group production sequence. Any component included in the group can be machined by that sequence, since the composite part covers all of the geometrical elements to be found in it.

Fig. 3.2 shows the setup for a capstan lathe, using the six positions of the capstan, the cross-slide and a thread-cutting attachment. The machine is set up to make the composite part; although the latter may not actually exist it is possible to machine all of the elements to be found in the group based on it, so that by setting up to machine the composite part it is possible to machine any component within the group. In other words, the machine is capable of making that specific group of components, and need not be set up from scratch; any component within the group can be machined after the appropriate adjustments have been made.

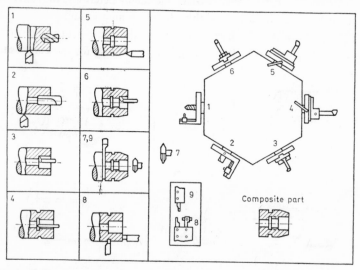

*Fig. 3.2* Setting up a capstan lathe to make the composite part

Whereas it may take 3–4 hours to set up a capstan lathe to make a single new component, the adjustments should only take 15–20 per cent of the time, since all of the tools and gauges are in position to make any component within the group.

When some of the tools included in the group setup are not required to machine one specific component they are excluded, and the cycle is confined to the necessary stages. It may be permissible in certain circumstances to change one of the tools, depending on the design of the component.

The concept of the composite part gives a good insight into the principle of group component machining, and is extremely useful during the early stages of familiarization with the principle of grouping and the drawing up of group production sequences.

In practice, the composite part is found to recede in importance as experience is gained in the practice of component grouping, especially when the individual components are themselves complicated, since it is not always possible to visualize a composite for such component groups. It may then be replaced by a small number of typical components, including the most complicated members of the group, or by single-operation composites, if it is not abandoned altogether. When skill has been acquired this does not occasion any difficulty; on the other hand it significantly widens the scope of the group technique.

# 4

## the organization of small- and medium-batch production on the basis of large-batch and mass-production principles

THE MANUFACTURE of any machine or instrument consists of the manufacture of the components and their assembly into the finished product.

Component manufacture usually proceeds through the stages of rough component production, machining, heat treatment, anti-corrosion treatment and decorative finishing, all in accordance with the specifications on the drawings.

The production sequences and tooling used to manufacture the components and assemble the machines or instruments are directly related to the complexity of the product, but are highly dependent on the batch size. Thus large-batch and mass-production can usually be organized on the basis of the most up-to-date techniques with a high level of mechanization and specialized high-productivity equipment (capstans, automatics, etc.), flowlines and conveyors.

The use of large numbers of attachments to make small batches is economically unsound, while for one-off production it is quite out of the question since the costs associated with making up the tooling cannot be recovered from sales. High-productivity automatics and capstan lathes are equally out of place in these conditions, since the time lost in resetting them between making successive batches of different components is not offset by the increased labour productivity over a short run. Batch-production plants are mostly equipped with centre lathes, millers, grinding and other general-purpose machines, operated by highly skilled workers.

Most of the items manufactured in small-batch plants are made as the need arises; the machine shops are not very highly mechanized and reliance is placed on the abilities of highly skilled operators. Consequently, the illogical situation is reached that there is no skilled production engineering section to back up the efforts of skilled design sections specializing in the basic products of the plant. Even such tooling as is specified in the production instructions is often not forthcoming when it is required, with the result that production is commenced without the correct tooling, delays in delivery are occasioned and a heavy price is paid for deviation from the correct procedure. Work must be rushed through, the quality of the product suffers, labour costs are increased, and on occasion all of the planning work already carried out is utterly wasted. The plant not infrequently has to introduce modifications to the product before the tooling for the first model has been completed.

The net result is that every time a new product goes into production — to say nothing of a large range of new products — the normal plant routine is disrupted with all of the consequences that that entails. This explains the extreme reluctance of managements to undertake new items of production, and it acts as a brake on technical progress.

It should also be pointed out that the plan for production preparation, which every enterprise must draw up annually, is reduced to nothing more than the issuing of prototype drawings and the approval for batch production of those items scheduled to be made during the current year, completely omitting the production planning aspects. This has an unfavourable effect on the level of mechanization in the plant and retards the increase of labour productivity.

Under the circumstances, it is essential for managements to look for new ways and means of organizing small-batch production.

What must be done, then, to make the use of high-productivity machine tools, conveyor assembly techniques and other progressive production techniques available to the small-batch production plant? It is essential to undertake a radical reorganization of small-batch and jobbing production on lines that will facilitate the adoption of the methods and organizational forms employed in large-batch and mass production.

Consider, for example, one particular case of reorganization, namely, the use of high-productivity equipment to machine components in small batches.

Table 4.1 lists a group of components that can all be machined on turret or centre lathes, assuming the production sequences to be planned individually (left-hand columns of the table). Every one of these components could be machined on turret lathes; centre lathes are used for some because the batches are so small. It is not always possible to make 6 or 12 months' supply of these components in one batch, because of the associated supply difficulties, apart from the fact that the machines are required to make other components.

Table 4.1 SAVINGS OBTAINED BY ADOPTING GROUP TECHNOLOGY

| Item No. | Component | Batch size | Individual sequences machine | cost (roubles) | Group sequences machine | cost (roubles) | Unit saving (roubles) |
|---|---|---|---|---|---|---|---|
| 1 | Mounting | 10 | Centre lathe | 0.24 | Capstan | 0.12 | 0.12 |
| 2 | Manifold holder | 100 | ,, | 0.25 | ,, | 0.19 | 0.06 |
| 3 | Pinion | 60 | ,, | 0.13 | ,, | 0.08 | 0.05 |
| 4 | Bevel gear | 150 | Turret lathe | 0.12 | ,, | 0.09 | 0.03 |
| 5 | Spur gear | 200 | ,, | 0.09 | ,, | 0.07 | 0.02 |
| 6 | Casing | 200 | ,, | 0.24 | ,, | 0.18 | 0.06 |
| 7 | Bearing housing | 50 | ,, | 0.20 | ,, | 0.10 | 0.10 |
| 8 | Flange | 115 | Centre lathe | 0.38 | ,, | 0.20 | 0.18 |
| 9 | Eccentric shaft | 25 | ,, | 0.15 | ,, | 0.09 | 0.06 |
| 10 | Shaft | 25 | ,, | 0.11 | ,, | 0.08 | 0.03 |

Even in batches of 50–60 off, machining on turret lathes is not an efficient method for these components, since the actual machining time is so short compared with the 3–4 hours required to tool up, set the machine and dismantle again at the end of the run. The machining costs are consequently quite excessively high.

The only way to lower the production costs is to reduce the tooling-up time between each batch of components or operations, and this can be achieved by increasing the batch sizes. How is this to be brought about in the small-batch plant? Group machining is the only solution.

In fact, when the components concerned were carefully studied in the light of the classification described above, it was found that 8 out of the 10 could be allocated into three groups, for machining by three group sequences. The first group included components Nos 1 and 3, the second Nos 4, 5 and 7 and the third Nos 6, 9 and 10. Components

Nos 2 and 8 remained for machining separately from the rest, using individual sequences.

Once the components had been classified, it was practicable to make them all on capstan lathes (right-hand columns of the table). The setting times for the capstan making each group were cut from 2–3 hours to 20–30 minutes, since each machine was already tooled up for the corresponding composite part and little time was taken in switching from one component within the group to another.

When in the course of time new components are brought into production they may prove to be similar to components already within the groups, so that they can be included with them to increase the batch sizes still further for the same production planning costs. As output expands and new products are added to the range, it may be found that components Nos 2 and 8 will eventually fit into new groups.

Thus, by changing the basis of production sequence planning from the individual component to groups it is possible to achieve appreciable savings, as indicated by the cost data included in Table 4.1.

# 5

# the use of group techniques in machining components on capstan lathes, centre lathes and milling machines

A SURVEY of the use made of capstan and centre lathes has shown that the selection of equipment during production sequence planning is based on batch sizes as much as on the complexity of the components, surface finish and accuracy. Small batches are most economically made on centre lathes.

As has already been pointed out, this has the result that individual production sequences drawn up for each component separately cannot take advantage of the benefits to be gained by using high-productivity capstan lathes; too much time is lost in the frequent retooling as one component follows another, and the equipment is standing idle for long periods.

When production is planned component by component, conditions militate against increased labour productivity from the capstan operators. The machining sequences are changed so frequently that they are unable to master the art of operating the machines at the necessary output rate. The type of work is constantly changing and there are insufficient skilled machinists available; consequently, as soon as a batch has been completed on one machine the operator must move on to another, which a skilled setter has been setting up for another component in the meantime.

The consequences of this situation are that the equipment becomes depersonalized, poorer performances are obtained, there are more frequent and prolonged waiting periods and stoppages for servicing, and the costs of keeping the machines in good order mount up.

The situation is significantly changed when the group principle is applied to component machining. The component production groups are set up in the following order of attack.

1 Collate the basic data, including the drawings of components for grouping, the scheduled outputs, the standard labour costs, and data on past rate fulfilment levels.
2 Examine the drawings for all of the components concerned and sort them roughly into classes.
3 Subdivide the components within each class into production groups.
4 Estimate the loads on the machine tools and correct the groupings in the light of the findings.

Production groups are formed within each class on the following basis.

1 The similarities between components in respect of design and operations required.
2 The batch sizes for the component groups (on the monthly and quarterly output scales).
3 The overall dimensions of the components.
4 The accuracy and surface finish required on different faces.
5 The nature of the rough components entering the machine shop.

It must not be overlooked that the size of any batch is determined by the time for which each production group will occupy the machines within a given period, whether week,* month or quarter.

We now turn to the particular problems of planning group production sequences for components made on capstan lathes.

The capstan lathe is a highly productive piece of equipment, adaptable to the use of multi-tool setups and sufficiently flexible to cover a wide range of complicated components; it combines high surface finish and accuracy with low machining costs.

However, before components can be machined on capstan lathes, a substantial time must be allowed for tooling up and setting the machines. Consequently, the majority of medium- and small-batch production plants reserve capstan lathes primarily for the simplest components

---

* The Russian term is 'decade', denoting the 10-day basic planning period. The week is normally used in English-speaking countries. – *Translator*.

such as bolts, studs, washers and bushes, or for roughing operations. The more complicated components required in small batches are made on centre lathes.

By adopting group techniques, however, it is possible to adopt capstan lathes for components irrespective of their complexity, even under small-batch conditions. The time expended in setting the machine and making the batch must of course be shorter than if a centre lathe was used. The important aspects are to reduce the time spent in setting the machines and familiarizing the capstan operators with the new working conditions. By drawing up the production sequences on group principles these problems can be successfully solved.

Experience in changing capstan lathes over to group machining has shown the following results.

1 Better use is made of the equipment, and the tooling and setting times are significantly shortened.
2 The level of mechanization is raised by adopting quick-acting high-productivity attachments capable of accommodating a range of different components.
3 The working conditions for the capstan operators approximate to those obtaining in large-batch production.

It must be borne in mind that when a given production group is made up of components for small-batch products, the number of different components required to keep the machine tool occupied will be larger than that when the components within the group are required for medium-batch products.

Under the former conditions the composite parts will usually be extremely complicated. The capstan will have to accommodate a large number of different tools, so that any component within an extensive group can be machined with a minimum of resetting time; this is an important aspect of component machining for small-batch products.

When each of the components is required in relatively large batches, the groups will include only a comparatively small variety before the machine is fully loaded. The group setting for components of the same complexity as before will include only a relatively small number of tools (Fig. 3.2). This type of setting will prove more productive than one designed to make all of the components within an extensive group.

The compilation of catalogues will be found useful in the systematic approach to group production sequencing. Armed with the catalogue, it is easy to trace the correct number and symbol for group operations required in new developments. The catalogue consists of a list of the group production sequences and settings currently in use in the plant, their names or symbols, sketches of typical components and brief notes on each production group.

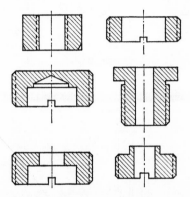

*Fig. 5.1* A group of simple components machined on capstan lathes

The following are a few examples of component groups taken from the Association catalogue and machined on capstan lathes.

The group shown in Fig. 5.1 consists of simple components, including threaded rings, nuts and bushes, mostly with slotted endfaces. The cross slides on the capstan lathes used for this group are fitted with special slotting attachments. The dimensional accuracy is Class 4 maximum, the surface finish Class $\nabla$ 5 maximum. The components are machined from bar stock up to 35 mm in diameter.

The group shown in Fig. 5.2 includes components of more complicated shape, but still axially symmetrical. They are classified as multi-stepped bushes, mountings and housings. These components are machined on vertical-head capstan lathes, equipped with an additional multi-position stop so that components with more shoulders can be machined. A special additional copy thread-cutting attachment is provided to cut two threads. The dimensional accuracy required is Class

3 maximum and the surface finish Class ▽ 7 maximum. The stock is held in a collet chuck, taking a maximum diameter of 45 mm.

Another group of complicated components is shown in Fig. 5.3.

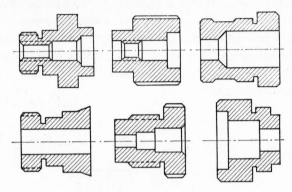

*Fig. 5.2* A group of more complicated components machined on capstan lathes

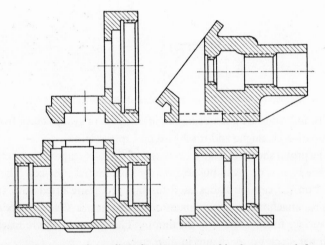

*Fig. 5.3* Another group of complicated components machined on capstan lathes

The capstan lathes are used only to machine certain of the surfaces on these components, to a maximum dimensional accuracy of Class 3 and surface finish of Class ▽ 6. The components are clamped in a special group chuck with interchangeable inserts, and consist of individual pressure diecastings or liquid-metal stampings.

The universal lathe is the most popular item of machine-shop equip-

Fig. 6.2 A slotting head for capstan lathes

Fig. 6.4 A work cabinet for storing tools

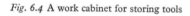

Fig. 6.3 A copy slide for cutting pairs of threads

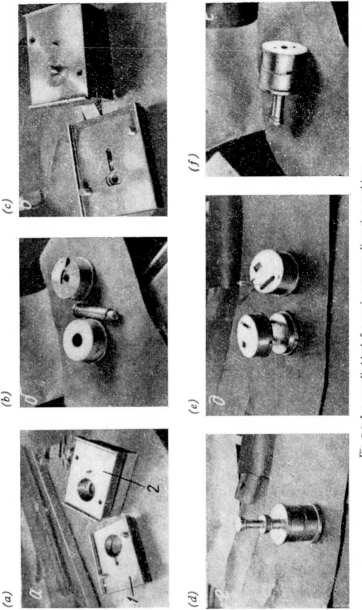

*Fig. 7.1* A group die block for use in pressure diecasting machines

ment in the industry, and is used particularly widely in jobbing and small-batch production. Its main use is for single-tool turning operations.

The use of ordinary universal attachments on lathes is associated with high costs in respect of auxiliary, setting-up and dismantling times. According to ENIMS,* centre lathes are at present in actual use for only 16 per cent of the available time; the rest is wasted in stoppages, auxiliary operations, setting up and dismantling after use. Bearing in mind that this figure relates to about 30 per cent of all of the machine tools in industry, one can clearly no longer tolerate the situation.

The enormous time losses experienced on centre and capstan lathes must be attributed to the fact that when production sequences are drawn up component by component it is impossible to allocate component groups to given machines. Consequently, when the turner has completed one batch of components he must turn to another that has nothing in common with the last, and must therefore spend a substantial time in resetting the machine.

The rational utilization of centre lathes is another problem that can only be solved by the large-scale adoption of group principles. After component groups have been set up and allocated to specific machines, consideration can be given to adapting the machines to the specific features of the group concerned. This simplifies production planning, since the basic attachments used in machining the group are permanently mounted on the lathe. The number of component settings is reduced, so that the dimensions are held more accurately and the skill rating for the job can be lowered.

Some of the centre lathes in the Association plants that have been turned over to group techniques have been fitted with turret heads (Fig. 5.4 facing page 5), transverse and longitudinal stops, three-position heads in the tailstock sleeve and other attachments to speed up the setting operations and to combine extended scope with specialization. This brings the mechanization of the centre lathe towards the level achieved in capstan lathes, and much higher labour productivities are obtained.

The reader might ask why one should adapt a centre lathe to convert it to a capstan lathe? Under the circumstances, the important fact to bear

* The Experimental and Scientific Research Institute for Machine Tools. – *Editor.*

C

in mind is that centre lathes account for about 30 per cent of all of the machine tools in industry, and the modifications are without doubt effective.

A number of examples of group turning sequences can be quoted from the catalogue drawn up within the Optical-Mechanical Association.

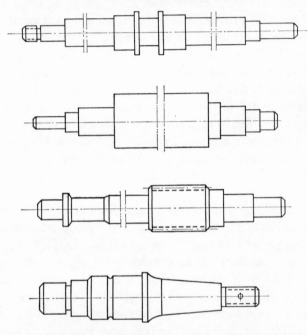

*Fig. 5.5* A group of shaft-type components for group machining on centre lathes

Fig. 5.5 shows a group of components of the shaft, rod, axle and screw type, with a length not exceeding 10–13 diameters. There may be several steps, grooves, profiled and tapered shoulders and recesses. This group of components is rough-turned ready for grinding on a Model 1E61 centre lathe equipped with a Model GS-1 hydraulic copying attachment. The dimensional accuracy is Class 3 maximum on diameter and Class 5 maximum longitudinally.

The group of bushes shown in Fig. 5.6 have numerous external and internal steps. The accuracy of the various diameters is Class 2–3, combined with tight tolerances on coaxiality of the internal and external surfaces. The maximum O.D. of the bushes is 90 mm and the maximum depth of the bore 50 mm. The piece blanks are supplied rough-machined with a final allowance of 1-2 mm. The Model 1E61 lathes used for finish machining are equipped with a four-position turret head, so that the components can be turned to a high level of accuracy and surface finish.

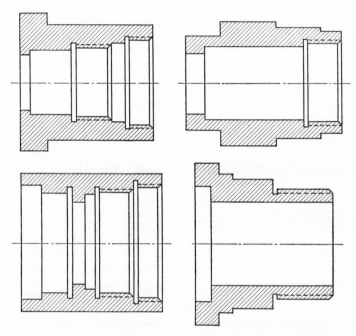

*Fig. 5.6* A group of complicated bushes for group machining on centre lathes

Various milling machines are also widely used in small- and medium-batch machine shops. There are similar major losses in respect of auxiliary, setting-up and dismantling operations on millers fitted with primitive universal fixtures. According to ENIMS, the actual operating time on millers is 40–50 per cent of working time available. The use of special fixtures involves much time in preparatory work and extra expenses are incurred, with the result that production costs are increased.

Group techniques offer a means of increasing labour productivity and reducing production costs on millers used in small- and medium-batch machine shops.

The components should be grouped in accordance with their design, the operations required, overall dimensions, methods of clamping in the fixtures and so on. In the design classification adopted within the Optical-Mechanical Association plants the components are divided into flat components the entire shape of which is obtained by milling, and complicated components only certain surfaces of which are milled. The operation classification is based on the type and size of the machine to be used, the types of milling cutter required and the reference faces and clamping details.

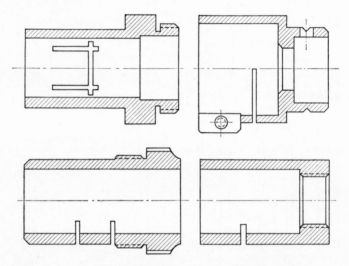

*Fig. 5.7* A group of components for group machining (slotted) on millers

The groups must be set up, as when grouping for centre and capstan lathes, with a view to keeping the machines fully loaded. Grouping components together because of similarities in one operation is not to be recommended, since this militates against the use of group fixtures and the miller can no longer be set up specially to machine a specific group.

Several groups from the catalogue used within the Optical-Mechanical Association for machining in millers will now be described.

The group shown in Fig. 5.7 is made up of components of cylindrical shape, mostly with thin walls. The maximum diameter is 60 mm and the maximum length 80 mm. The operations of milling the longitudinal and transverse slots are carried out in a group fixture on horizontal millers.

The keys grouped together in Fig. 5.8, most of them made from brass, have two inclined flanks; again they are milled in a group fixture, following machining of the top and bottom faces and the endfaces on other machines. The two inclined flanks are milled in a group fixture in a permanently set vertical milling machine, using cutter heads 200–250 mm

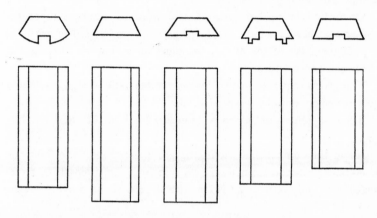

*Fig. 5.8* Another group of components for group milling

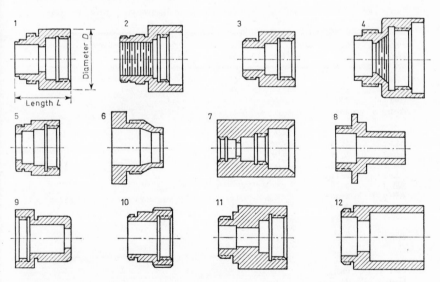

*Fig. 5.9* A group of components requiring the same group machining sequence

in diameter. The component dimensions are width 4–30 mm, length 20–150 mm and thickness 12–16 mm.

The working documents form an important aspect of the introduction of group techniques. Accordingly, we shall now consider a typical form and order of drawing up the instructions for machining a group of components on capstan lathes.

On the basis of the classification for the proposed group of components linked together by similarity of operations, sketches are prepared of typical members of the group, to obtain an outline characteristic as described above (see p. 19).

The group sequence known by the symbol 1-GP-9 signifies 'No. 1 machine shop, group sequence No. 9'.

The components machined by sequence No. 9 are illustrated in Fig. 5.9.

All of the components within the group must meet the following conditions: external diameter $D$, 28 mm maximum; length $L$, 1.5 $D$ maximum. Only one thread is cut with the aid of the copying attach-

Table 5.1 LIST OF COMPONENTS MACHINED BY ONE
GROUP SEQUENCE

| | | | | Group symbol 1-GP-9 | Machine shop No. 1 |
| --- | --- | --- | --- | --- | --- |
| Product No. | Component No. | Product No. | Component No. | Product No. | Component .............. No. |
| A–1 | 19 | G–1 | 91 | N–1 | 6–1 |
| A–1 | 127 | G–1 | 98 | N–1 | 7–1 |
| A–1 | 197 | | | N–1 | 7–5 |
| A–1 | 223 | | | N–1 | 7–8 |
| | | GZh–1 | 1–16 | | |
| | | GZh–1 | 1–18 | | |
| AE–7 | 1–23 | GZh–1 | 1–21 | | |
| AE–7 | 1–29 | GZh–1 | 2–17 | | |
| AE–7 | 1–33 | GZh–1 | 2–35 | | |
| AE–7 | 2–11 | GZh–1 | 2–69 | | |
| AE–7 | 2–19 | | | | |
| AE–7 | 2–20 | | | | |
| AE–7 | 2–27 | M–1 | 41 | | |
| AE–7 | 2–35 | M–1 | 42 | | |
| | | M–1 | 56 | | |
| G–1 | 26 | M–1 | 57 | | |
| G–1 | 35 | M–1 | 82 | | |
| G–1 | 38 | M–1 | 83 | | |
| G–1 | 68 | | | | |
| G–1 | 79 | | | | |

ment in each capstan operation. The maximum permissible difference between external diameters is 16 mm in not more than four steps, for each of the capstan operations. The accuracy is Class 3 maximum on not more than two diameters for each capstan operation, and the other diametral and linear dimensions are to Class 4 maximum. The surface finish is Class ▽6 maximum for components made from steel or silumin and Class ▽7 maximum for brass and duralumin. A Class ▽7 surface finish is permitted over an external length of not more than 5–6 mm on steel components.

The list of items that can be machined by group sequence 1-GP-9 (Table 5.1) includes all of the components in production at present. In time, the list will be extended by adding new components.

The next document relating to group machining sequence 1-GP-9 is the list of attachments (Table 5.2) common to all components in the group. The term 'attachment' in this case covers the jigs, fixtures, cutting tools, gauges and auxiliary tools, classified into those permanently mounted on the machine tools used for this particular group and the interchangeable items brought into use when machining some specific component.

The instructions card for machining this group (Table 5.3) relates to the composite part or the most complicated member of the group. The instructions cards for other members of the group are simplified versions (Table 5.4), and no particular skill is required to draw them up.

Fig. 5.10 shows how the machine tool is set up for the group sequence. The setting relates to the composite part and is based on the entire group of components that can be machined by group sequence 1-GP-9.

Table 5.2 LIST OF GROUP ATTACHMENTS (COMMON TO
ALL COMPONENTS)

| Attachments | | | | Auxiliary tooling | | | |
|---|---|---|---|---|---|---|---|
| Item | Symbol | Opera-tions | No. in use | Item | Symbol | Opera-tions | No. in use |
| Permanent | | | | Interchangeable | | | |
| Chuck | N40–5 | 2 | 1 | Sleeve | N47–5 | 2 | 1 |
| Holder | N15–5 | 2 | 1 | Bush | N2–5 | 2 & 3 | 2 |
| Post | N16–5 | 2 | 2 | Cam drum | N163–5 | 2 & 3 | 2 |
| Post | N17–5 | 2 | 2 | Cam die | N92–5 | 2 & 3 | 2 |
| Post | N18–5 | 2 | 2 | Sleeve | N160–5 | 3 | 1 |
| Post | N19–5 | 2 | 2 | Sleeve | N152–5 | 3 | 1 |
| Post | N20–5 | 2 | 2 | Roller holder | UP–899 | 3 | 1 |
| Post | N21–5 | 2 | 2 | | | | |
| Post | N22–5 | 2 | 2 | Roller holder | N131–5 | 3 | 1 |
| Post | N23–5 | 2 | 2 | | | | |
| Post | N24–5 | 2 | 2 | | | | |
| Holder | 6N1–5 | 2 & 3 | 2 | | | | |
| Holder | UP–911 | 2 | 2 | | | | |
| Slide | N101–5 | 2 & 3 | 7 | | | | |
| Toolholder | N112–5 | 2 & 3 | 4 | | | | |
| ,, | N113–5 | 2 & 3 | 4 | | | | |
| ,, | N114–5 | 2 & 3 | 4 | | | | |
| ,, | UP–898 | 3 | 3 | | | | |
| Post | N179–5 | 2 & 3 | 2 | | | | |
| ,, | N83–5 | 2 | 1 | | | | |
| Stop | UP–879 | 2 & 3 | 2 | | | | |
| Bush | GN38–5 | 2 & 3 | 2 | | | | |

Table 5.2 (*Continued*)

| | | | | Group symbol 1–GP–9 | Operations 2 & 3 | Machine shop No. 1 | |
|---|---|---|---|---|---|---|---|
| **Tools** | | | | | | | |
| *Item* | *Symbol* | *Operations* | *No. in use* | *Item* | *Symbol* | *Operations* | *No. in use* |
| **Permanent** | | | | **Interchangeable** | | | |
| Cutter | $\frac{10 \times 10}{N71\text{-}1}$ | 2 & 3 | 8 | Cutter | N79-1 | 2 & 3 | 2 |
| Cutter | $\frac{10 \times 10}{N72\text{-}1}$ | 2 & 3 | 8 | Drill | $\frac{GOST}{887\text{-}41}$ | 2 & 3 | 2 |
| Cutter | $\frac{10 \times 10}{N73\text{-}1}$ | 2 & 3 | 5 | Drill | N10-1 | 2 & 3 | 2 |
| Cutter | $\frac{10 \times 10}{N74\text{-}1}$ | 2 & 3 | 1 | Drill | N9-1 | 2 & 3 | 2 |
| Cutter | $\frac{10 \times 10}{N75\text{-}1}$ | 2 & 3 | 1 | Cutter | N325-1 | 2 & 3 | 2 |
| Cutter | $\frac{8 \times 60}{N93\text{-}1}$ | 2 & 3 | 2 | Cutter | N98-1 | 2 & 3 | 2 |
| Cutter | $\frac{T15K6}{10N266\text{-}1}$ | 2 & 3 | 4 | Cutter | N80-1 | 2 | 1 |
| Cutter | $\frac{T15K10}{10 \times 50}$ | 2 & 3 | 4 | Cutter | N84-1 | 2 & 3 | 3 |
| Cutter | $\frac{N267\text{-}1}{VK8\text{-}12}$ | 2 & 3 | 2 | Cutter | N85-1 | 2 & 3 | 4 |
| Cutter | $\frac{10 \times 60}{N273\text{-}1}$ | — | — | Cutter | N339-1 | 2 & 3 | 4 |
| Cutter | $\frac{T15K6\text{-}8}{10N309\text{-}1}$ | 2 & 3 | 2 | Cutter | N86-1 | 2 & 3 | 2 |
| Cutter | T30KU-8 | 2 & 3 | 2 | Cutter | N87-1 | 2 & 3 | 2 |
| Cutter | $\frac{10 \times 50}{N315\text{-}1}$ | — | — | Roller | N225-1 | 3 | 1 |
| | | | | Roller | N21-45 | 3 | 1 |

# Table 5.3 MACHINING INSTRUCTION CARD

| Machine shop No. 1 | Product AV-15 | Component 15-61 | Name Bush | Operations 2 |
|---|---|---|---|---|
| EQUIPMENT | | | MATERIAL | |
| Equipment type, works or firm | Capstan | | Grade | Steel 20 |
| No. of components machined at once | 1 | | Attachment Name | Symbol |
| | | | Collet chuck | N-16 |

| Operations | No. of surfaces machined | Tooling names and symbols Auxiliary | Cutting | Measuring |
|---|---|---|---|---|
| 1. Feed stock to stop | | Sleeve N47-5 | — | — |
| 2. Rough turn $D_1$ (allow 0.5 per side) and drill $d_1$ through | | Drilling bush N10-1 | Drill $d_1$, N10-1 | — |
| 3. Finish turn $D_1$ and drill $d_2$ to length $l_3$ | | — | Drill $d_2$, N10-1 | Calliper $D_1$ and plug $d_1$ and $d_2$ |

# Table 5.4 SIMPLIFIED MACHINING INSTRUCTIONS CARD

| Group 1-GP-9 | Product A-1 | Component 223 | Material Steel 20 | Machine shop No. 1 | Equipment Capstan | Operations 2 |
|---|---|---|---|---|---|---|

∇5

Engineering sketch with dimensions: $120°$; $2M20 \times 1$; $\phi 15^{+0.12}_{+0.04}$; $\phi 20.2^{+0.52}$; $8^{+0.36}$; $14^{+0.43}$; $2^{+0.25}$; $42.5_{-0.62}$; $\phi 11^{+0.7}$; $\phi 25_{-0.28}$

| Operations | Tooling |
|---|---|
| 2 | Sleeve 28N47–5 |
| | Bush 10 × 15N2–5 |
| | Bush 11 × 15N2–5 |
| | Cam drum L2N163–5 |
| | Cam die L2N92–5 |

| Operations | Cutting tools |
|---|---|
| 2 | Drills 10N10–1 & 11N8–1 |
| | Cutters $\dfrac{2 \times 10 \times 10 \times 40}{N86-1}$ & $\dfrac{12 \times 1 \times 15°}{N98-1}$ |

| Opera-tions | Instructions | Opera-tions | Gauges |
|---|---|---|---|
| 2 | Turn by group sequence 1-GP-9, to dimensions in sketch | 2 | Plug 15A4; plug for 2M20 × 1; internal gauge 20.2AgN34–2; plug 2M20 × 1; plug 42.5Br; templates A–1–223–1k & A–1–223–2k. |

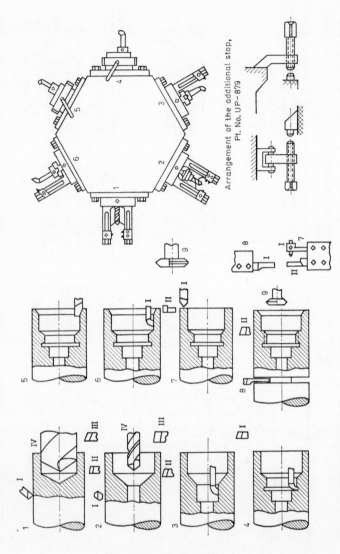

Arrangement of the additional stop,
Pt. No. UP-879

*Fig. 5.10* Capstan lathe set up for group machining

# 6

# the group technology
# section

CAPSTAN LATHE section No. 2 was selected for the introduction of group technology within the Optical-Mechanical Association plants. The change-over to group machining on the capstan lathes was effected over a period of 3–5 months by a team comprising four production engineers, two jig designers and two capstan setters. The 30 group sequences drawn up in the section covered a total of 2800 different components.

Experience in setting up this section has demonstrated that the following principles should be adopted in drawing up group machining sequences for capstan lathes.

1 The machine-setting operations involved in changing over from one component to another in the same group should be simple enough to be carried out by semi-skilled operators within a short time.

2 The adjustments required to machine any component in the group should not involve much more than changing the positions of the longitudinal and diametral stops.

3 The tooling mounted permanently on the capstan lathe should be capable of machining any component within the group concerned. The interchangeable tooling for specific components should not exceed 10–15 per cent of the entire setup in the capstan head.

4 Every time the machine is changed over to another component in the group an effort should be made not merely to reset in the minimum time but to reduce the actual machining time for the component concerned. This involves supplementing the standard

cutting tools with special profile tools and combination toolholders so that more than several surfaces can be cut simultaneously.

5 The components should be grouped with a view to avoiding by-passing any of the capstan head positions or reversing back to them.

By adopting group machining in small- and medium-batch machine shops, it becomes possible to specialize every workplace.

The group attachments should be designed with the following essential points in mind:

1 Quick-acting clamping attachments for every component in the group should be permanently mounted on the machine.

2 It should be possible for a relatively unskilled operator to set the tools to dimensions every time the component is changed, and to achieve the required level of accuracy and dimensional stability.

Accordingly, when the capstan lathes were changed over from component-by-component operations to group sequences, their productivity was raised by providing the following attachments.

1 *The group collet chuck* (Fig. 6.1) is pneumatically operated and can be fitted to capstan lathes with vertical capstan heads. It is designed for the machining of cylindrical components from piece blanks.

The design of the chuck is as follows. The fixed section consists of a faceplate 1, rigidly attached to the lathe headstock casing, in which the pneumatic cylinder is housed. The latter comprises the cylinder 2 and the endcover 3. The piston 4 slides along the cylinder under the air pressure, and its motion is transmitted through the ring 12 and balls 5 to the bush 6. Two diametrically located grooves are machined on the inside face of the bush 6, running in opposite directions. The chuck body 9 is screwed on to the lathe spindle and centred by the bored hole D. The sleeve 8 fits on the outside of the body 9, and the bush 6 on the sleeve 8. An annular recess on the body 9 houses the two semicircular rings 7 with the cylindrical pins 13. The complete ring 7 and its pins 13 can rotate freely in the recess in the body 9. When the air pressure moves the piston 4 to the left, the bush 6 travels with it. Pins 13 move along the helical grooves in the bush and carry the sleeve 8 to the left. The ring 11 bolted to the end of the sleeve 8 is displaced relative to the tapered faces of the collet 10 in which the component is held.

2 *The slotting attachment* (Fig. 6.2 facing page 20) is used in the machining of threaded rings with slots to take a screwdriver. Slot-milling is normally an independent operation carried out on milling

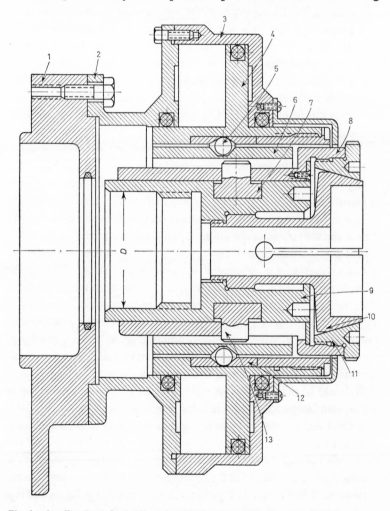

*Fig. 6.1* A collet chuck for holding piece blanks of large components

machines, and must then be followed by a finishing operation on the thread. By means of this attachment slotting can be carried out in the capstan lathe before the thread is cut, so that a subsequent finishing operation is avoided.

3 *The copy slide* (Fig. 6.3 facing page 20) is capable of cutting two concentric threads at a single component setting. The threads can be both external, both internal, or one of each. Apart from increasing the labour productivity by reducing the number of component settings, this attachment meets the conditions that the threads must be concentric with each other and with respect to the other cylindrical surfaces machined at the same setting.

4 *The multi-position machine stop* for lathes with vertical capstan heads replaces the normal radial stop. A range of different diameters can be obtained by adjusting the stop screws, using the same cutting tool throughout.

Special attention was devoted to workplace organization during the change-over to group techniques. For instance, work cabinets have been constructed with compartments for the tools (Fig. 6.4 facing page 20), so that a complete set of cutting and auxiliary tools can be kept in readiness at the workplace for the group of components allocated to it.

The performance figures for the section over the years have indicated major savings and a substantial increase in the output. Taking the saleable output of the section for 1957 as 100 per cent, the figures have risen to 112 per cent in 1958, 124 per cent in 1959, 132 per cent in 1960 and 150 per cent in 1961. The capstan operators have been raised one grade higher. Moreover, by concentrating on specific groups of components the operators have acquired a certain skill, and as a result the scrap rate has been reduced by 40 per cent.

It should be pointed out that whereas at least one out of the group of six capstan lathes was always idle for resetting when components were machined one by one, the entire capstan section is now fully loaded, since the time to change over from one component to the next has been drastically cut and the operators themselves are undertaking some of the setting work. The number of toolsetters has been halved and two capstan sections have been brought together, releasing two chargehands and two work distributors. Planning has been substantially improved as well, since all of the machines are permanently allocated to specific groups and specific operators.

The figures in Table 6.1 indicate the savings achieved since the change-over to group machining.

Naturally, as with any other innovation, certain difficulties were encountered during the organization of group technology, and some malcontents wanted to carry on in the traditional way. On the other hand, there was no shortage of enthusiasts who appreciated group methods as a novel approach to production organization and technology. They were able to see beyond the organization of group techniques on the capstan lathes towards the shops and works of the future, run entirely on this progressive principle.

Table 6.1 SAVINGS ACHIEVED BY ADOPTING GROUP MACHINING

| Machines | Factors reducing costs | Time saved % |
|----------|------------------------|--------------|
| Capstans | Reduction in resetting times | 40 |
| | Reduction in machining times | 33 |
| | Reduction in labour costs | 55 |
| | Reduction in tooling costs | 46 |
| Centre lathes | Reduction in machining times | 27 |
| | Reduction in special tooling costs | 80 |

D

GROUP PRODUCTION ORGANIZATION & TECHNOLOGY
By. E. K. IVANOV. translated by E. BISHOP & J. GRAYSON.

# 7

# the use of group techniques in the manufacture of pressure diecastings and liquid-metal stampings

THE LOWERING of production costs constitutes one of the basic economic criteria of plant performance. Cost-cutting problems are usually tackled by driving the metal-cutting equipment and tools harder. The machines are given higher rotary speeds and the cutting tools new shapes. The main effect of this is to cut the machining time, which of itself accounts for but a small proportion of the total time spent on component manufacture. The amount of swarf removed is not reduced and the proportion of metal utilized remains invariably low.

To get to the roots of the problem of cutting labour costs one must look to the use of progressive blank-forming techniques capable of producing rational blanks with minimum machining allowances, and with surface finish and shape very close to those of the finished component. A composite answer to the problems of saving on metal, reducing the amount of swarf removed and increasing the proportion of metal utilized should also be sought in the rationalization of blanks.

Progressive blank-forming techniques employed by plants within the Association include pressure diecasting, investment casting, liquid-metal stamping, shell moulding using resin-bonded sands and cold extrusion. This chapter is concerned with the forming processes most widely used in these plants, namely pressure diecasting and liquid-metal stamping.

*The pressure diecasting process* is widely used in all spheres of industrial production for making components of complicated shape. The following factors have contributed to its wide-scale adoption.

1 High productivity of the process.
2 Good surface finish of the castings (Class $\triangle$ 5).

3 High dimensional accuracy (Class 4 or 5).

4 Short production cycle.

5 Opportunity of producing cast assemblies.

6 Good properties of the casting material resulting from the fine-grain size after solidification in the heat-conducting die.

Besides being highly accurate, pressure diecastings have identical measurements, and so their accurate reference faces can be used during machining. The small machining allowances (not more than 0·5 mm per side on dimensions of better than Class 4 accuracy) minimize the amount of machining required.

Pressure diecasting has been widely adopted principally in mass and large-batch production plants. Until recently it was thought to be unprofitable for the manufacture of small batches of components (say up to 500 per annum) because of the high labour costs involved in making the tooling. But the group approach to production has put a different complexion on matters and high-productivity progressive methods can now be profitably applied to the manufacture of blanks in small batches.

Group technology can be applied to pressure diecasting by using group tooling (group die blocks), in which different-shaped components can be produced by means of interchangeable inserts, instead of by making special tools for each separate component.

As in the case of machining, the components must be subdivided into groups before the group tooling is designed. The design and operation characteristics constitute the basis of the component groupings.

The design classification of the cast components includes the following.

1 Line at which the die is parted to produce the cast component.

2 Ejector system used in the die to extract the casting.

3 Location of the casting in the die.

4 Overall dimensions of the components.

The operations classification includes the type of gating system used.

The die parting line actually determines the location of the casting in the die and therefore the type of ejector system used to extract the casting. The overall dimensions of the casting govern the size of the die block and type of pressure-diecasting machine used. The type of gating system used affects the quality of the casting and the die block design.

The parting line can run either across one of the casting endfaces, in which case the external outline of the cast component will be formed in one half of the die, or across the biggest overall cross-section of the casting, in which case the external outlines of the casting will be formed in the moving and stationary halves of the die.

If the forming takes place in the stationary half the casting is ejected by the plate, but if it takes place in the moving half or both halves ejectors perform this operation.

Castings made in group die blocks can be gated from the side or middle. The following general points should be borne in mind when the gating position is chosen.

1   Central gating is always preferable because it reduces the overall dimensions of the die block.
2   The gating system is designed so that the stream of metal entering the die systematically forces the air out of the die cavity towards the parting line.
3   If possible the gate should enter one of the faces to be machined.
4   The thickness of the ingate should be 25–30 per cent that of the casting wall (a typical thickness for the casting is 6–7 mm).

The parting line constitutes one of the most important factors in the grouping of the components, since it determines the die block design, the location of the casting in it and the type of ejector system employed.

The role of the die block ejector system is by no means unimportant, because if the casting is housed in the stationary half of the die removal with a plate is infinitely preferable to removal by ejectors, otherwise ejection marks will be left on the casting.

Another decisive factor in the grouping of components is the overall size of the casting, since its projected area at the parting line constitutes the basic criterion for selecting the type of machine to be used. The overall dimensions do not, however, affect the basic die block design; all that they do is determine the number of standard block sizes required.

The gating system influences the grouping of the components, because the castings can be gated centrally or from the side.

Components can be classified at each individual plant on this basis with due regard to the special production characteristics obtaining. Appropriate groups can then be set up.

In the Association plants the components are grouped on the following basis. The first group consists of castings produced in dies, where the parting line runs across an endface of the casting. The complete casting is located in the stationary half of the die and is ejected from the core by a plate. It is arranged for central gating.

The second group again consists of castings produced in dies, where the parting line runs across an endface of the casting. The complete casting is located in the stationary half of the die and is ejected from the core by a plate, but is arranged for side gating.

The third group consists of castings produced in dies, where the parting line runs across either an endface or one of the casting cross-sections. The casting is located in either the moving half or the moving and stationary halves of the die; it is ejected by ejectors and is arranged for central gating.

The fourth group has the same characteristics as the third, but is arranged for side gating.

The time taken to make the interchangeable inserts is 15-20 per cent of that to make the dies. Fig. 7.1a shows the group die block used to cast components of the second group. (Figs 7.1a – 7.1f are to be found facing page 21.) In this die block a side gating system is provided. The parting line runs across the endfaces of the components, which are ejected by a plate. The casting is located in the stationary half of the die. The stationary part of the die block 1 attaches to the stationary part of the machine and has a locating system and clamping means for the interchangeable inserts.

The moving part of the die block 2 attaches by its base to the moving part of the machine and also has means for locating and clamping the interchangeable inserts.

The inserts for each component (Fig. 7.1b) have locating elements in the form of accurately machined cylinders with shoulders. Fig. 7.1c shows the die block assembled and ready to be placed on the machine, and Figs 7.1d, e and f show sets of inserts for other components.

The inserts used in the group die block for casting components of the second group (Fig. 7.2 facing page 52) can be changed without the block being taken off the machine. The big advantage of this type of die block is that inserts for casting new components can be changed without the bother of taking the block off the machine and then replacing and locating it. All that has to be done to change inserts 1 and 2 is to remove side clamps 3 and 4 and tighten up side stops 7 a little. The inserts are located with the two halves 5 and 6 of the die joined together.

Substantial savings accrue from the use of group tooling instead of separate dies. A single-purpose die for casting a comparatively simple component costs 350–400 roubles* to make, against 250–300 roubles for a group block; the set of interchangeable inserts costs 50–100 roubles.

Another point worthy of note is that the use of die blocks halves the time required to design new dies.

Group technology has made pressure diecasting in batches of 100 castings per annum a profitable process. The use of group techniques will greatly extend the range of application of this progressive method and set the stage for its large-scale adoption in small-batch production.

Liquid-metal stamping for non-ferrous alloys is bound to take the place of drop forging because the piece blank is replaced by a measured portion of liquid metal. The process combines the basic advantages of casting and drop forging and is capable of producing blanks with a Class 5 surface finish and Class 5–7 dimensional accuracy. It should be regarded as a casting process, because it embodies all of the phenomena associated with casting, e.g. shrinkage, solidification and liquid-metal flow.

Compare liquid-metal stamping with pressure diecasting. The basic concept of liquid-metal stamping is that metal freely poured into the open die cavity is displaced (extruded) under the action of the punch, fills the die cavity and solidifies under pressure. The solidification of the metal under pressure produces sound thick-walled castings. The casting assumes its final shape after the die has been closed.

In liquid-metal stamping the punch is lowered quite slowly giving sufficient time for all of the air to escape from the die cavity, especially

---

* The official Soviet exchange rate is one new rouble for one American dollar, although the *true* value of the rouble may vary considerably depending on the type of product being considered. At the time of going to press the sterling exchange rate was $2.40 (U.S.A.) to £1.0..0. (U.K.)

as the liquid metal is poured straight into the die, with the result that the volume of air in the die is greatly reduced. This factor combined with the application of the plunger pressure provides conditions conducive to the production of sound castings, since the pressure applied to the molten metal is maintained until the casting has completely solidified.

The walls of components produced by liquid-metal stamping can be quite thick; the thicker the walls the less will be the shrinkage defects, because the plunger pressure is maintained until the castings solidify and so prevents blowholes forming.

Fig. 7.3 contains sketches of the metal-pouring setups used in liquid-metal stamping. This process differs from pressure diecasting in that in

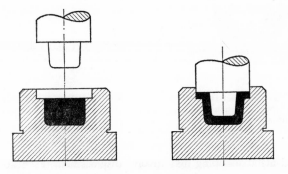

*Fig. 7.3* Metal pouring setup for liquid-metal stamping

the latter the metal is fed into the die through a gating system. In pressure diecasting the metal enters at high speeds and so the air in the cavity is not always able to escape. Any that is left in the die gets into the more massive sections of the casting and forms blowholes in them.

In modern hydraulic pressure diecasting machines the specific pressure in the compression chamber ranges from 350 to 1,000 kg/cm$^2$ and so the air trapped in the blowholes will experience similar pressures. This inevitably restricts the use of pressure diecasting for alloys that are to be heat-treated, because any subsequent heating will reduce the strength of the cast metal with the result that it may no longer be capable of resisting the expansion of the air in the blowholes and the casting will swell, warp or distort,

In pressure diecasting high specific pressures are applied while the castings are solidifying, but these pressures are not maintained until the castings have completely solidified because the ingates used in pressure diecasting solidify before the casting. Pressure diecastings should therefore have fairly thin walls (2–6 mm thick). With wall sections of this order there is little risk of shrinkage defects.

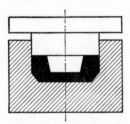 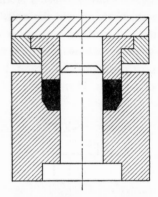

*Fig. 7.4* Liquid-metal stamping with extrusion and solidification under pressure

*Fig. 7.5* Liquid-metal stamping without extrusion, i.e. merely solidification underpressure

Liquid-metal stamping may involve displacement (extrusion) of the metal and solidification under pressure (Fig. 7.4) or merely solidification under pressure (Fig. 7.5).

In the case of liquid-metal stamping with extrusion (displacement) of the metal, the punch closes on the bottom half of the die and occupies the space previously filled with metal, forcing the liquid metal upwards until it fills the remaining cavity. Thus, the pressure applied initially to the metal is consumed in displacing it, i.e. in forming the outline of the casting. The working pressure energy that is consumed will, however, be negligible, since the metal is displaced while still in the liquid state.

The moment the metal has filled the die cavity the pressure forces increase sharply, and at that moment all sections of the die cavity will be positively filled. However, in view of the fact that the metal is still in the liquid state the liquids can be regarded as being virtually incompressible. There are still no volumetric changes in the casting at this stage of blank production. It is only when solidification commences that the pressure compresses the casting and eliminates the gas and shrinkage defects.

In liquid-metal stamping accompanied only by solidification under pressure there is virtually no displacement of the liquid metal. All that the applied pressure does initially is to fill the die cavity more positively with the liquid metal. The casting solidifies under plunger pressure during the subsequent pressing stage.

Components are made in a range of non-ferrous alloys by the liquid-metal stamping technique, which is carried out on either hydraulic or friction presses. The process makes high demands on the dies both as regards the precision with which they are made and the strength of the material used in them, since they are expected to operate under high concentrated loads and specific pressures. The dies are fairly expensive to make and the associated labour costs are high, so they are used mainly in the production of blanks required on large batches. Thus liquid-metal stamping, in which blanks of measured diameter and length are replaced by measured portions of molten metal, has come to replace drop forging.

In drop forging, several dies are usually needed to produce a blank of complicated shape, the piece blank being forged in one die after another. In liquid-metal stamping, however, there is no need for roughing dies because the portion of metal poured into the lower half of the die assumes the shape of the die cavity, and the pressure energy consumed in imparting the final shape to the blank will be negligible.

From the cost standpoint the replacement of piece blanks with measured portions of liquid metal is very effective, because melting stock costs far less than non-ferrous bar stock.

One of the main ways of putting liquid-metal stamping to profitable use in small-batch production conditions is to standardize certain assemblies and entire dies. Group technology can help to solve this problem and extend the use of liquid-metal stamping to small-batch production.

The grouping of components stamped in liquid metal on friction presses is based on their design characteristics, which constitute the basis for designing the group dies.

The blanks produced by liquid-metal stamping are usually free from recesses, undercuts or projections to interfere with their extraction from the solid halves of the die, or the extraction of the punch from the blank. They include axially symmetrical components with flanges or shoulders, and components of rectangular, square or other cross-sectional shape.

On this basis the classification covers two groups of components, the first axially symmetrical and the second with shaped cross-sections, the material of the casting not being a determining factor because it does not affect the die design.

The first group includes axially symmetrical components up to 140 mm in diameter and 90 mm in height. The second group covers copper and aluminium alloy components of squat, flat or elongated shape, not longer than 140 mm, not more than 40 mm in height and with a stamping area of up to 140 cm². The groups can differ from plant to plant, or be based on other variables, depending on the production conditions.

The design of the group dies provides for the use of interchangeable inserts to give a range of component shapes. Since the design does not include extractors, the inserts are given draws sufficient to retain the component in the bottom half of the die, from which it can then be removed with an ejector or by hand. The punch has draws of 3–5° and the die draws of 0·5–1°.

Water-cooling is provided in group dies to stabilize the operating temperatures and to prolong the life of the inserts.

Preference should be given to flash dies when selecting the die design as they are more reliable in operation.

Circular inserts are provided for the production of axially symmetrical components and rectangular inserts for components of rectangular cross-section.

Experience has shown that the application of group technology to liquid-metal stamping in group die blocks gives the following results.

1 The range of components that can be produced by this technique is extended.

2 Production is made more flexible by virtue of the fact that the ability to manufacture the blanks does not depend on the availability of bar stock of the appropriate diameter.

3 The material costs in liquid-metal stamping are lower because secondary alloys are used instead of bar stock; furthermore, compared

with the manufacture of components from bar stock, liquid-metal stamping gives a 40–45 per cent saving on the weight of metal used and a 15–20 per cent reduction on machining times.

4 There is no longer any need to cut bar stock in the rough component shops.

5 The time spent in designing the tooling is reduced because the inserts are much simpler in design than the separate dies.

6 Steel 50 can be used instead of grade 6Kh2V8 steel for making the inserts; provided that the group block is cooled efficiently the die life is hardly affected. The replacement of steel 6Kh2V8 with steel 50 gives a substantial saving, bearing in mind that the first costs 1 rouble per kg and the second only 10 kopeks.

Group technology applied to liquid-metal stamping has made the process profitable for batches as small as 100 castings per annum.

# 8

# the use of group technology in finishing, assembling and other production processes

SUCCESS IN the application of group technology to machine-shop and foundry processes led to the idea that it might succeed equally well in woodworking, painting, varnishing, electroplating and assembly operations.

The adoption of group technology in finishing operations would be tremendously significant since this type of work accounts for a large proportion of the production costs in engineering and instrument-making plants, by reason of the fact that the work is not so well organized as that in the machine shops.

A salient point here is that in small- and medium-batch shops, i.e. where the components are being turned out in small batches, it is impossible to keep a plating bath operating for any length of time under one set of conditions and it will seldom be fully loaded. Frequent interruptions occur in operation because of the need to prepare the workplace for treating each new component.

Opportunities of using attachments and mechanizing the manual labour in painting and varnishing operations on small batches of components are limited. The production planning required for electrostatic spray painting on an individual component basis is costly in both time and labour, because each component requires a specifically designed suspension.

In other words the lack of a systematic approach to the planning of production sequences in shops where many types of similar components are produced with the same type of finish results in an unwarranted variety of production sequences, and this complicates the task of the production engineers, the shop planning and progress staff, the rate setters and the foremen. The documents for the individual production sequences are cumbersome and take a long time to prepare, and if the range of components is large they are awkward to use and store.

Group production setups for finishing work allow whole groups of components to be processed under the same plating-bath conditions, so that the proportionate time during which they are in use can be increased. Group production sequences applied to the painting of components permit the wide-scale adoption of a range of attachments to mechanize the manual labour.

The following working documents are required to convert finishing operations to the group process: instructions on the procedure to be adopted for different kinds of finishing; and the group production finishing sequence.

Separate instructions on how to set about the various kinds of finishing process are issued for each type of finish. They specify all of the operations required in the type of finishing concerned, the type of equipment, attachments, bath compositions, chemical consumption rates, bath operating conditions, and the procedure for making up and maintaining the solutions and electrolytes, types of scrap and methods of eliminating them, and the main points regarding safety measures and labour protection. The foreman, production engineer or operator can then check at any moment on the correctness of the process conditions.

The availability of all of the information required in the instructions rules out the necessity of repeating them for each component. This is taken care of by the group production sequence, which includes all of the components subjected to a given type of electroplating or painting and requiring for this purpose identical conditions and sequences for carrying out the process.

Thus, in electroplating work, for example, it is very important that the surface areas to be plated on the components loaded into the baths shall be identical, or similar within certain limits. In this case the current density and plating time are regulated in accordance with these variables for each group. For paint finishes it is important to group components requiring the same preparatory treatment and having similar surface areas.

The group sequence contains a brief description and specification of each process, the sequence and nature of all of the preparatory operations for the type of finishing concerned, a calculation of the surface areas, an annotated list of the group attachments to be used, and the standard times and rates for the group of components.

Thus the adoption of group technology in finishing operations offers scope for the following savings.

1 Substantial reduction of the production documentation.
2 Simplification of the rate fixing, the rates being set for the group rather than for each individual component.
3 Reduction of the number of types of finishing attachment by replacing the individual with group attachments.
4 Increased labour productivity by reducing the time spent on setting up and dismantling and increasing the skill of workers specializing on particular components within the group concerned.

One of the group attachments extensively used in finishing operations on components processed on the group basis (Fig. 8.1) is intended for chromium-plating flat steel components on which one of the faces must be left free of chromium.

The attachment is designed on the magnetic contact principle and comprises two suspensions 10, terminating in uprights 1, which are linked by rods 3, carrying four magnets 8 made of the special AMKO-4 alloy. Four steel strips 2 (two on each side) are brought up to the magnets and tightened. Rod 9 links the uprights and stiffens the structure. Dura-lumin tube 4 and intermediate strips 5 and 6, which fit on rod 3, are used to locate the magnets. Rods 3 and 9 are secured to the uprights by nuts 7. The components for chromium-plating are laid on the steel strips 2 and held there by the force of the magnets. On completion of the plating process the strips 2 are withdrawn from the magnets 8 and the components are removed from the strips.

Group techniques have also been adopted in planning the conditions in an anodizing transfer line. The line comprises a series of baths arranged in an order specified by the group production sequence for anodizing aluminium alloys. The durations of each stage of the treatment, which must be the same for the entire group of components, are set out in the form of a cyclogram, which is used as the programme for the automatic equipment.

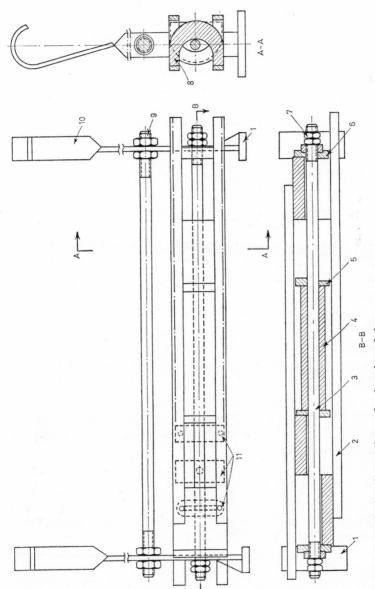

*Fig. 8.1* A magnetic clamping attachment for chromium-plating

The preset programme for the sequence of group production operations in the anodizing process is carried out automatically with the aid of stepping selectors, and components are transferred from one operation to the next by the automatic transfer equipment. A group anodizing attachment (rack) is designed to handle any component within the group concerned, and can accommodate 48 small or 24 large components at a time.

The types of anodizing carried out on aluminium-alloy components were standardized when the group to be finished on the automatic equipment was formed. A single sequence was established instead of the four applied previously, and was used to set up the entire process for that group.

Fitting and assembly work in engineering plants normally accounts for 30–40 per cent of labour costs, but the level of mechanization of this type of work is low, especially in small- and medium-batch plant. The adoption in small-batch production of the techniques of mass production will facilitate the mechanization of fitting and assembly jobs.

At plants within the Association it has proved possible in drawing up group production sequences for fitting and assembly work to base the grouping of the entire range of products on the similarities between the production problems to be solved for similar items. With that end in view a composite product consisting of the maximum number of production assembly units and with the most complicated system of assembly was worked out for each group. The composite products were divided into production assembly units and group job cards were prepared for them.

The group production documentation comprises a classification system, the group production sequence for assembling the product, and group cards for the unit and final assemblies. By planning the working documents along these lines it is possible to assemble several similar instruments or machines by the same group production sequence, and the availability of the sequences used for different products reduces production planning time and eliminates repetition.

When new instruments or machines go into production it must first be decided whether they fit into any group of existing production sequences. If they do, the production planning will be greatly simplified

Fig. 7.2 A group die block with cassette-type inserts

Fig. 9.1 A group lathe chuck

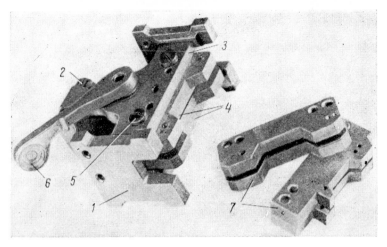

*Fig. 9.2* A group jig with interchangeable strips

*Fig. 9.3* A group milling attachment

and the planning time cut to between a third and a quarter of its former value.

The group production sequence used to assemble the objectives for more than 100 different types of microscope made within the Association constitutes an instructive example.

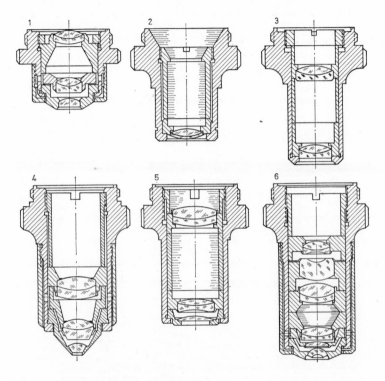

*Fig. 8.2* A group of objectives suitable for assembly on a group basis

The objectives all have different arrangements and functions, and the most typical layouts are shown in Fig. 8.2. To work out an assembly sequence for all of the objectives one must start with the most complicated, which can be referred to as composite objective 6. To assemble it one must perform virtually all of the operations required to assemble any objective within the group. Accordingly, taking the composite objective, a detailed production sequence is drawn up to include every operation, each of which has its own number (Table 8.1).

E

Table 8.1 LIST OF CODIFIED OPERATIONS

| Operations | Description of operation | Code symbol |
|---|---|---|
| 1 | Boring aperture and lens recess in front lens mounting | 20GP-6-1 |
| 2 | Fitting, centring and fixing front lens in mounting | 20GP-6-2 |
| 3 | Cleaning and polishing mounting for chromium plating | 20GP-6-3 |
| 4 | Chromium plating mounting with front lens | 20GP-6-4 |
| 5 | Cleaning mounting and lens after plating | 20GP-6-5 |
| 6 | Preparing front lens and mounting for blooming | 20GP-6-6 |
| 7 | Blooming front lens | 20GP-6-7 |
| 8 | Boring aperture and lens recess in meniscus lens mounting | 20GP-6-8 |
| 9 | Fitting, centring and fixing meniscus lens in mounting | 20GP-6-9 |
| 10 | Undercutting air gap in meniscus lens mounting | 20GP-6-10 |
| 11 | Preparing meniscus lens for blooming | 20GP-6-11 |
| 12 | Blooming meniscus lens | 20GP-6-12 |
| 13 | Boring aperture and lens recesss in compound lens mounting | 20GP-6-13 |
| 14 | Fitting, centring and fixing compound lens in mounting | 20GP-6-14 |
| 15 | Undercutting lens mounting to maintain air gap | 20GP-6-15 |
| 16 | Preparing compound lens for blooming | 20GP-6-16 |
| 17 | Blooming compound lens | 20GP-6-17 |
| 18 | Assembling objective to correct air gap | 20GP-6-18 |
| 19 | Cleaning objective | 20GP-6-19 |
| 20 | Assembling objective | 20GP-6-20 |
| 21 | Adjusting objective | 20GP-6-21 |
| 22 | Centring and facing objective to height | 20GP-6-22 |

Table 8.2 CODE SYMBOLS OF OPERATIONS USED IN
ASSEMBLING A GROUP OF OBJECTIVES

| Code symbol | Objectives | | | | | | |
|---|---|---|---|---|---|---|---|
| | 1 | 2 | 3 | 4 | 5 | 6 | |
| 20GP-6-1 | ╱ | | | ╱ | ╱ | | ╱ |
| 20GP-6-2 | ╱ | | | | | | |
| 20GP-6-3 | ╱ | | | | | | |
| 20GP-6-4 | ╱ | | | | | | |
| 20GP-6-5 | ╱ | | | | | | |
| 20GP-6-6 | | | | ╱ | | ╱ | |
| 20GP-6-7 | | | | ╱ | | ╱ | |
| 20GP-6-8 | | | | | | ╱ | |
| 20GP-6-9 | | | | | | ╱ | |
| 20GP-6-10 | | | | | | ╱ | |
| 20GP-6-11 | | | | | | ╱ | |
| 20GP-6-12 | | | | | | | |
| 20GP-6-13 | ╱ | ╱ | | ╱ | | | |
| 20GP-6-14 | ╱ | | | | | | |
| 20GP-6-15 | ╱ | | | | | | |
| 20GP-6-16 | ╱ | | | | | | |
| 20GP-6-17 | ╱ | | | | | | |
| 20GP-6-18 | ╱ | ╱ | | ╱ | | ╱ | |
| 20GP-6-19 | ╱ | ╱ | | ╱ | | ╱ | |
| 20GP-6-20 | ╱ | ╱ | | ╱ | | ╱ | |
| 20GP-6-21 | ╱ | ╱ | | ╱ | | ╱ | |
| 20GP-6-22 | ╱ | ╱ | | ╱ | | ╱ | |

The sequences to be employed in assembling any of the other objectives shown in Fig. 8.2 can be found from Table 8.2, which denotes the numbers and sequence of all of the operations required for assembling the objective concerned.

For products that cannot be assembled by using existing group production sequences, the production planning is carried out as for a new group sequence.

Besides cutting the time spent on production planning, changing over from individual to group production sequences for fitting and assembly work affords an opportunity for mechanizing the manual work and designing high-productivity tooling.

The adoption of group assembly techniques is closely related to the problems of unification and standardization. Moreover, the introduction of group assembly and machining sequences again includes the drawing up of group component catalogues, which can be referred to in designing new articles.

PRODUCTION ENGINEERING RESEARCH ASSOCIATION
OF GREAT BRITAIN
MELTON MOWBRAY,
LEICESTERSHIRE.

# 9

# group tooling

ONE OF the main advantages of the group approach is the tremendous saving in the time and costs involved in the preparations for production, in which the design and manufacture of the tooling incur the highest labour costs.

In medium- and small-batch plants employing individual methods of component manufacture the tooling costs are apportioned to a comparatively small output, which of course raises the unit costs quite considerably. The result is a lowering of the level of mechanization, which militates against any increase in labour productivity.

In other words the current practice of designing and making the tooling on an individual basis is to some extent at variance with the problems of raising labour productivity and cutting production costs.

The group approach to the manufacture of components radically alters the situation. The attachments are now designed not for one but for a group of components, brought together and grouped on a design and operations basis. The tooling costs can be spread over a much larger output and the unit costs are reduced in proportion.

Success in the adoption of group machining techniques will depend very much on how well the group attachments are designed. These are used to machine the components in specific groups, for which they have been designed. The components can be machined with or without the aid of extra adaptors (inserts), depending on the design of the attachment and the components in the group. The inserts in most cases are of simple design and inexpensive to make.

The group attachments must provide rapid and accurate setting-up of all of the components in the group concerned, and the component clamping arrangements must be accessible, simple and reliable. The attachments themselves should be assembled from parts that are not costly to make, but that are quite rigid. At the same time they should be compact, designed for easy swarf removal and precise in operation.

Given an adequate range of group attachments the time spent on planning new production will be greatly reduced, since it will no longer be necessary to design and make large numbers of special complicated attachments. All that need be done is to design and make simple interchangeable inserts.

Group attachments can be designed for lathes, millers, drilling, unithead and other machines and used to machine components in metals, glass and other materials, depending upon the type of production. Under the conditions obtaining within the Association they are all basically attachments of average complexity regardless of the diversity of design. Because the group attachments are used to machine large numbers of components whose range may be added to, thereby giving rise to frequent changes of the inserts, the insert recesses must be heat-treated, accurate and highly finished. Well designed group attachments and inserts are very efficient in operation, and it is no longer necessary to change the whole attachment to reset the machine.

The design of the group attachment is based on a carefully chosen group of components and a group production sequence drawn up beforehand that indicates the equipment for the operation concerned. The job card sketch must indicate the reference and machining faces, and the component should be shown in the form in which it arrives for machining in the group attachment.

The general drawing of the group attachment indicates the co-ordinate dimensions to the contact and reference faces or other insert locating points, and the tolerances on the dimensions should conform to the machining accuracy required with due allowance for the dimensional scatter of the components before machining. In addition, a brief description is given of how to use and set the attachment, together with specimen designs of the interchangeable inserts to facilitate subsequent design work.

Much thought should be given to the design of the fixed or adjustable clamp used to secure all of the components of a given group in the attachment, if possible without extra inserts. The design of the counterweight, which may be interchangeable or adjustable, must also be well thought out, to provide for the possible addition of inserts.

When group multi-position attachments for milling machines are designed, special consideration should be given to the reliable location of every component in the group on its reference face.

In group jigs the body and mechanical clamp are fixed, and the referencing inserts, plates and bushes are interchangeable. The jigs should be light and stable, with easy setting of the component, and with provision for swarf removal. The inserts for all of the group attachments should be simple to make and must consist of as few parts as possible. The seating and locating points should be heat-treated and accurately machined and finished.

As the group tooling stocks build up and specialized experience is acquired in this field catalogues of group attachments should be compiled by means of a systematic classification based on the design and operations required, with a view to preventing repetition of similar designs when starting up new production. A brief description should be appended to the drawing of each attachment in the catalogue, covering its layout and operation, with the limiting dimensions of the components that it can accommodate.

In cases where there are several attachments of similar design, a full description is given for the first and followed by the distinguishing features of the remainder. The catalogue contains the most original universal attachments used in group production sequences, together with a description of their layout and operation.

The group attachments described below are taken from the catalogues used in the Association.

Fig. 9.1 (facing page 52) shows a group lathe chuck for machining non-cylindrical components. The chuck can be mounted on a centre or capstan lathe and consists of a body 2 with a square 6, which has a precision groove for seating and locating the interchangeable insert-element 7. The interchangeable inserts 9–16 are held in the chuck by means of screw 8, and are changed when changing from one component to another. The component 5 is secured by means of a lever system, comprising lever 3, clamp 4 and rod 1, which is linked to a pneumatic power unit mounted at the end of the lathe spindle.

The group jig in Fig. 9.2 (facing page 53) can be used for drilling or countersinking holes in flat and narrow components up to 8 mm thick. It is designed so that the drilling or countersinking can be done on two sides without the component being taken out of the jig. The jig consists of body 1, with a lug in which the jaw 3 can rotate about shaft 2, over a limited angle.

The component is placed between two interchangeable strips 4 and located by hand with the aid of stops. The interchangeable strips 7 are secured with four screws 5, one to body 1 and the other to jaw 3. The component is clamped by turning hand lever 6, which has a thicker section at the end in the form of a bush with two threads, an external left-hand and internal right-hand. The left-hand thread screws into jaw 3, and the right-hand thread screws on to a pin built into the body 1 of the jig. With this combination of two threads the component can be tightly clamped or rapidly released by a relatively small movement of the lever.

The function of the group milling attachment in Fig. 9.3 (facing page 53) is to clamp prismatic components for milling flats or slots. The attachment consists of a plate 11, on which is mounted body 1. In the body there are two vertical grooves, one straight and locating the slide 3 and the other inclined and locating the slide 6. The two slides are linked by means of a yoke and frame to the pneumatic power unit on the machine. Components for machining are placed and located on interchangeable supports 5 and clamped by two interchangeable jaws 4 and 8, which are secured by means of thumb screws 2 and 7.

When the slides 3 and 6 move downwards under the action of the power unit the component is clamped between jaws 4 and 8 by the action of the inclined groove and, conversely, when they move upwards it is released. The attachment can be adjusted with regulating screws 9 and 10. The clamping force is 800 kg.

The group jig shown in Fig. 9.4 (facing page 68) is used to drill holes in flat broad strip-type components. It comprises a base plate 1, which has four built-in legs 4. The plate 1 has an opening to accommodate the interchangeable jig plates, which are clamped by screws 2 and 7, and the component is secured by means of a pivot strip 5, turnscrew 6 and wing nut 3.

The interchangeable jig plates have identical overall dimensions for every component within the same group and can be prepared beforehand. The sizes of the interchangeable inserts and their arrangement on the jig plate correspond to each individual component in the group.

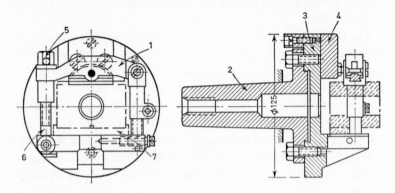

*Fig. 9.5* A lathe group attachment

The lathe group attachment in Fig. 9.5 is intended for use in the machining of small body components on centre lathes. The attachment comprises a body 3, centred and mounted on the tapered mandrel 2, which is inserted in the lathe spindle. On the body of the attachment there is a small table with an accurate slot in which the interchangeable insert 7 with locating elements can be secured. The component is secured by bracket 1 with the aid of nut 5 and rotary pin 6. The function of counterweight 4 is to balance the attachment on the lathe.

# 10

# the modification of equipment in group production conditions

MODIFICATION CAN extend the scope, substantially raise the productivity and bring the technical characteristics of machine tools up to date. Until recently, however, most of the modification carried out was aimed at making maximum use of the latest cutting tools, i.e. increasing the capacity, operating speed and rigidity of the machines.

The use of high-speed and high-power cutting conditions has substantially reduced the actual machining time but has had comparatively little effect on the overall component machining times.

On most of the metal-cutting machines now used in engineering and instrument-making the machining time accounts for less than 25 per cent of the total working time, so future improvements to equipment should be directed towards cutting the auxiliary time.

In other words the modification of equipment should not be restricted merely to increasing the speed and capacity for the purpose of cutting the machining time; the aim must be to cut auxiliary time too by mechanizing and automating the machines and by using quick-acting attachments, and by reducing the setting-up and dismantling times by the use of rapid setting-up techniques.

A number of plants and various production innovators are attempting to solve these problems by modifying equipment and automating machine tool control, but sometimes not enough thought is given to the problem or the designer is out of touch with the work to be done on the machine concerned. There have been frequent cases of machines being modified and automated at tremendous expense and all to no avail, because afterwards the modified assemblies and units do not participate fully in the manufacture of the components to be machined on the piece of equipment concerned.

Thus if modification is to raise productivity, a system must be created capable of modifying every machine tool in line with the job it performs.

The component group machining method can provide the solution to this very important problem. Once all of the components have been grouped according to the type of machining, shape and production characteristics, machine tools can be modified for a production sequence that will provide high-productivity machining of the components in the group concerned.

In this method of production planning the machine is fitted with only those mechanisms and automatic equipment required to ensure high-productivity machining of any component in a specific group or number of groups.

The basic directions for modifying the equipment are then solved in the process of drawing up the group production sequence. Each machine is earmarked for one or more groups of components, with the result that large numbers of speeds and feeds are not needed, the movement cycles of the working parts of the machine are simplified, the stage is set for increasing the capacity and speed, and the problems of automation are made much easier to solve.

The nature of machine tool specialization is determined by the specific production and process requirements that arise when the group production sequence is drawn up. The choice of machine to be modified is determined by the equipment available.

For instance, when machining multi-stepped bushes, rings, flanges' gears and the like on centre lathes, it is a very good idea to provide the machine with multi-tool front and additional rear slides, multi-position longitudinal and transverse stops, and a pneumatic clamping system. The provision of these attachments makes the machine capable of carrying out several operations at one setting, thereby increasing the labour productivity for machining such groups of components by 25–30 per cent.

It is worth while to equip centre lathes used for the manufacture of stepped components such as axles, worms, stepped shafts and bushes, with hydraulic copy slides (Fig. 10.1, facing page 68). In the case in point the copying device is a flat profiled template or standard component over which a follower passes, transmitting the outline of the standard component or template by means of the hydraulic attachment and cutter to the rough component and thereby imparting the required shape to it.

The hydraulic copy slide is very rarely used in small-batch production conditions because it takes so long to set up and dismantle, and the saving resulting from the reduction in component machining times cannot be justified. But when the group principle is applied to component manufacture the use of hydraulic copy slides increases labour productivity by 30–40 per cent.

When drawing up group production sequences for machining components on capstan lathes it is usually possible to design a range of special attachments and additional working parts to provide the most rational utilization of the machines and so reduce the setting-up time.

Since the rational sequential selection of the group in group machining substantially increases the effective batch sizes, the stage is set for the use of specialized unit-head machine tools providing high-productivity machining of every component in the group even under small-batch conditions.

The unit-head machine shown in Fig. 10.2 (facing page 69) is built up from standardized units and is used for cutting shaped slots and plane surfaces. The components are machined at one setting. The machine has five power heads mounted on special brackets, and a circular indexing table accommodating six clamping attachments. The power heads operate simultaneously with overlapping machining times.

The entire machining cycle has been mechanized. The heads are switched on and off and reset, the table rotated and the components clamped and released automatically in accordance with a preset programme, so that the operator has merely to take the machined component off and set up the next blank.

The group attachment used on this unit-head machine is designed so that it can be reset for the other components in the group by using interchangeable elements without removal from the machine, so that very little time indeed is required to reset for the next component in the group.

Transferring the machining of components from millers employing individual production sequences to a unit-head machine operating on the group principle has given a time saving of 50–60 per cent.

# II

# programme-controlled
# machine tools

THE LARGE-SCALE adoption of the group machining method is preparing the way for automating the operating cycle of universal equipment by
the use of programme control.

The plants in the Association have a large number of programme-controlled centre and capstan lathes. It is only justifiable to use these
machines in small-batch production conditions if group machining
techniques are employed. The substantially higher labour productivity
that results from one operator looking after two machines, the improved
quality of output and the reduced production costs occasioned by the
comparatively low expenditure on materials offer tremendous opportunities for setting up sections and even whole plants consisting entirely
of programme-controlled machine tools.

The programme controller designed and successfully introduced for
the new capstans shown in Fig. 11.1 (facing page 69)* can be modified
to suit other types of capstan lathe. The lathe can operate under automatic or semi-automatic conditions and is used for diametral dimensions
to Class 3 accuracy and linear dimensions to Class 4 accuracy; it provides Class $\nabla$ 6 surface finishes on steel and Class $\nabla$ 7 on non-ferrous
metals.

The working parts of the lathe are moved automatically by means of
special pneumatic-hydraulic and pneumatic drives controlled by valves,
which in turn are controlled by electromagnets with solenoids energized
via a system of relays in a given sequence related to the operating programme to which the lathe is set. The operating programme is drawn up
in accordance with the machining sequence for the component con-

* These lathes were made within the Optico-Mechanical Association.

cerned and establishes the sequence of movements of all of the working parts on the machine and the main drive switching sequence. The programme is fed into the controller, which comprises a system of type MKU-48 relays, a stepping selector and a contact panel with several rows of tumbler switches. Each row of tumblers has the function of selecting the programme of the next element in the automatic cycle. The normally open contact is closed when the appropriate tumbler is switched on, thus preparing the associated relay for operation.

The programme is read by the stepping selector. The various relays controlling the solenoids are combined in eight groups, corresponding to the eight tracks in the stepping selector. Each group is connected to the corresponding selector tracks via the first contacts in the tumblers on the control panel. The second contacts in the tumbler switches are connected to strips across the stepping selector. Thus the first strips in each track of the stepping selector form the first line across it, the second the second and so on.

When the programme has been selected by switching on the appropriate tumbler and the required tools and mechanical stops have been set in position, the lathe is ready for action. When the machine is switched on, feedback sensors signal the execution of the present movements or the resetting of the controls. The sensors are standard MP-1 and KV9-A microswitches, mounted on the paths of the lathe-operating mechanisms. On receipt of the signal that an order has been properly carried out it is picked up by the stepping selector, and a ratchet moves the sliding contact to the next strip. This operates the next relay, the tumblers for which have been set in accordance with the programme. The circuits are prepared for the next stage in the automatic operating cycle, and so on.

The setting up of the lathe is a simple job, well within the operator's capacity.

The following slight modifications have been made to the lathe to provide an automatic operating cycle.

1 An extra drive has been provided to speed up the initial forward and rapid return strokes of the turret slide, while the existing feed mechanism is used for the working strokes.

2 The cross slide, which formerly could only be traversed by hand,

has been provided with an extra drive to give a working feed and speed up the traversing in either direction and resetting to centre.

3  The manual control system has been improved, the automation including the changing of speeds and feeds, the clamping and release of the turret, the feed and clamping of the material, and the starting, reversing and stopping of the motor.

The capstan lathe converted for programme control is still set basically as for an ordinary lathe; the operator merely sets up the tools and adjusts the stops.

Experience to date in operating the programme-controlled capstan lathes indicates a saving of about 3,000 roubles per annum on each machine as a result of the reduced basic and auxiliary times and the fact that one operator can supervise two machines. The cost of the modifications, including all of the controls and circuit arrangements, is 1,500 roubles, and takes only six months to recover.

Another point not to be overlooked is that on programme-controlled machines the same regulated rhythm of operation is maintained throughout the working day. The operator does not have to expend a great deal of physical energy and can concentrate on supervising the operation of the machines.

The programme-controlled centre lathes in operation at the Association plants are fitted with the numerical programme control system developed at the 'Lenpoligrafmash' Works in 1960. A standard 45-column punched card is used to carry the programme. The assemblies and mechanisms of the system were made on a centralized basis; they are intended for modifying two types of centre lathe, one with 150-mm bed clearance (Model 1E61) and the other with 200-mm bed clearance (Model 1A62). The first system has an SVP code and the second, an SVPU.

There is no space here to describe the layout or principles of operation of the modified lathes; descriptions have been given elsewhere.* It will however be useful to discuss some of the conclusions and considerations arising from the 18 months' experience gained in operating them at plants within the Association.

* M. E. Barksii. Production sequence planning and programme preparation for centre lathes with numerical programme control. LDNTP, 1961. (In Russian.)

It should be mentioned that initially every plant experienced major difficulties in installing, commissioning and operating these lathes. There were quite a number of reasons for this. First, the operators' inadequate knowledge of the design and operating principles of the various units and mechanisms led to difficulties when they were originally allocated to the lathes. Second, certain units and mechanisms gave poor performances, especially the electrical equipment on the machines. Third, unskilled workers were employed to install the units on the lathes, and in some cases badly worn machines were earmarked for modification without preliminary overhauls. Fourth, insufficient thought was given to the organization of the loads on these machines, which resulted in long stoppages and a need to use them to make comparatively simple components.

There are now about 40 programmed machine tools operating at plants within the Association. They have all been concentrated in separate sections, where they are operating on the closed production cycle principle together with other machines.

Experience has proved that it does not pay to operate machines with numerical programme control in small numbers (at least 8–10 machines should be used). The machines will function well only when given proper care and supervision by maintenance fitters familiar with their layout and working principle. It is best to assign a special electrician fully conversant with electronic systems to maintain the electrical side of the machines. Two machines should be allocated to each operator and arranged so that he or she can easily supervise them both.

More attention must be paid to the question of the work loadings on machines using group production techniques.

Plants in the Association have discontinued the practice of making only simple shaft-type components on programme-controlled machine tools. Now the task has been undertaken of machining the most complicated components within the scope of SVP and SVPU system machine tools (excluding screwcutting, taper turning and so on) with numerical programme control. For this purpose all of the components selected for transfer to the programme-controlled machines are grouped according to their design, the operations required and the appropriate machining sequence in the light of the complexity, the accuracy of diametral and axial dimensions and the surface finish.

The duration of the machining cycle for each operation was also taken into consideration when the components were grouped. Since every operator is in charge of two machines it is essential that the groups of components allocated to each machine should, besides having similar tooling setups, facilitate loading and unloading without greatly increasing the idle time.

Particular attention must be paid to the production planning and the preparation of programmes for centre lathes with numerical programme control. There are major difficulties, for the work is extremely time-consuming. It usually takes a production engineer several hours to draw up the programme instructions for a single component, and sometimes a complete working day for components with large numbers of operations and transfers. The job is extremely tiring, requires the utmost concentration and can be entrusted to only highly qualified engineers.

In other words, the high production planning costs reduce the cost effectiveness of machines with numerical programme control. Hence great urgency attaches to the problem of reducing the labour costs involved in drawing up programme instructions.

The radical solution would be to use electronic computers for this purpose. The basic information for compiling the programme manuscript would be fed into the computer, which would complete all of the necessary mathematical calculations and issue the final programme carrier with the lathe-operating programme recorded on it. In practice, however, this method of drawing up programmes still presents a number of difficulties, and although research is now in progress in this direction the results will not be known for a considerable time.

Production engineers and designers in the Association are currently collaborating with the Technology Faculty of the Leningrad Institute of Engineering Economics (LIEI) in the design of a relatively simple piece of equipment which will substantially, although not completely, mechanize the work of production engineers in compiling programme instructions. Labour costs of this work will then fall, and the use of centre lathes with numerical programme control in production will then be a paying proposition.

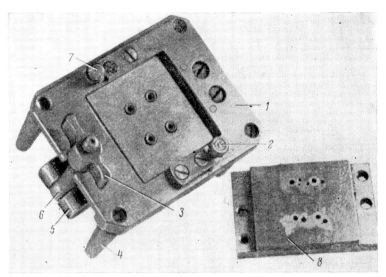

*Fig. 9.4* A group jig

*Fig. 10.1* A centre lathe fitted with a hydraulic copy slide

*Fig. 10.2* A special unit-head machine for milling shaped slots

*Fig. 11.1* Capstan lathes fitted with programme controllers

# 12

# the group technology shop

PLANTS OPERATING in the field of group technology design group production sequences for given types of equipment, depending on the type of production involved. At instrument-making and engineering plants, where capstans, centre lathes and milling machines predominate, it is best to begin planning group production sequences with the capstan lathes because in small- and medium-batch shops these machines are very unproductive.

The inclusion of a group technology capstan section in a machine shop with other types of equipment will simplify the job of converting the other machines to group techniques. The increase in the wages and skill ratings of the workers in the first group technology section to be set up, i.e. the capstan section, will facilitate the future extension of the change-over and ensure its success. The obvious saving, the increased labour productivity and the increasingly responsible attitude of the staff and shop-floor workers will arouse the interest of the entire shop in group technology.

These very favourable circumstances for converting the manufacture of components by group machining techniques to other types of equipment must be utilized to expedite the task of setting up a group technology shop, bearing in mind that the job of converting a shop to this technology is a major undertaking dependent on the co-operation of every employee in the plant.

In the case in question all of the basic measures such as the modification of equipment, design of unit-head machines and group tooling, and changes in the production organization setup should be carried out under the supervision of the plant management, trade unions and party

F

organizations. The entire staff of the plant must give undivided attention to the task of setting up the group technology shop, and it should take priority in the organizational and technical development plan.

To organize the conversion of an entire shop to group technology on a proper basis, a special group technology office should be set up in the chief production engineer's department. The engineers who handled the conversion of the capstans to operation on group principles from the design stage to the shop-floor should be transferred to the chief production engineer's department so that their experience can be utilized.

After the capstan lathes have been converted to group machining methods, the next group of machines whose conversion to group technology would give the maximum economic effect is selected in accordance with the local conditions. The milling machines were second on the list at the plants in the Association.

In small-batch production conditions, the components (bodies, brackets, etc.) are milled on general-purpose machines, such as universal, horizontal, vertical and bench millers. Such components are usually clamped for machining direct on the table of the milling machine; sometimes, however, complicated expensive universal attachments are used.

This technique of machining components in small-batch plants makes it necessary to employ highly skilled workers, and involves a high expenditure of auxiliary, setting-up and dismantling time; the labour productivity is low and the component manufacturing costs are high.

Special as well as universal attachments can be used to increase the labour productivity, but their use involves production engineering departments and toolrooms in more difficulties and does not always achieve its main object of substantially raising the labour productivity. This is because with small batches of components the machining times per operation are quite short, while the production of the attachment and the setting-up, adjustment and dismantling operations take up a great deal of time. Moreover, when a batch of components has been completed, the entire machine must be reset.

The conversion of milling machines to operation using group production sequences makes it practicable to go over to group instead of costly individual attachments. They should meet the following requirements.

1 The group attachment should provide accurate setting and clamping of every component in the group.

2 The setting and clamping of the various components within each production group in the group attachment should be done with the aid of adjusting devices, interchangeable assemblies and group attachment components. The interchangeable assemblies and components may take the form of rings, inserts, strips and brackets.

3 The setting-up of the attachment for machining any component in the group should be simple, within the scope of a 2nd–3rd grade milling machine operator, and should not take longer than 5–10 minutes.

4 The group attachment should produce component dimensions of the required accuracy and stability.

5 The group attachment should be quick-acting, of simple design and easy to operate.

The group machining of components affords scope for using the most effective method of machining on millers, i.e. continuous milling. Fig. 12.1 shows the attachment used for the continuous milling of plane surfaces on a vertical miller. The attachment is mounted on a continuous rotating circular table, which is driven by the machine. The table has eight fixed clamping attachments spaced equally around the circumference of the body 1, one of which is always loaded. The clamping setup comprises two jaws 2 and 3 mounted on slides 4 and 5, which can move up or down in sloping grooves. When the movement is downwards the jaws close up and bring the inserts together, gripping the components for machining. The inserts are mounted on a small fixed table 6. The slides are operated by means of a pneumatic piston 7 linked to the slides by arm 8 and plunger 9.

Air is supplied to the pneumatic cylinders via a distributing cone 10 and the ducts 11, automatically releasing or clamping the jaws when the attachment reaches the loading position. The attachment table rotates continuously and has two speeds, one of 2, the other of 4 rev/min. Sixteen components are machined per revolution, as each insert holds two components. Single-place inserts are designed for the larger components and the loading of the components is also continuous.

A 250–300 mm diameter end mill with 6–8 teeth is used as the cutting

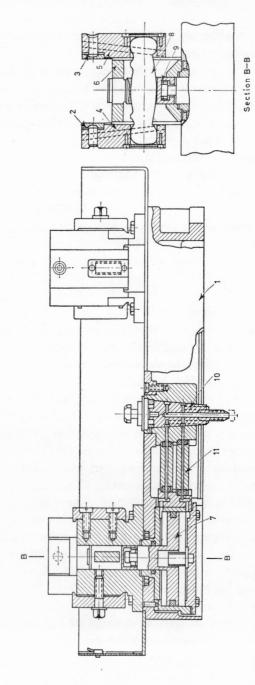

Section B–B

*Fig. 12.1* An attachment for continuous milling

tool. The attachment is used for milling medium batches of components, mainly in brass or aluminium alloys.

Group miller attachments are replacing a large range of single component and universal attachments. When introducing new articles the components can be machined on the existing group attachments by making new interchangeable parts, thus cutting the production planning time by 50–60 per cent and sometimes more.

The conversion of the capstans, millers, centre lathes and drilling machines to group machining at the majority of engineering and instrument-making plants would cover nearly the entire range of equipment in the machine shops. The organization in a plant of even a single group technology shop marks a major, useful and necessary step forward.

The operation of shops on group principles affects the work of the production planning, chief production engineer's and supplies departments and requires from them attention, better organization of production preparation, accurate planning and well-organized supplies of materials and blanks.

A group technology shop has been operating for several years in the No. 2 plant of the Leningrad Association of Optico-Mechanical enterprises and its performance gives a good idea of the effectiveness of this progressive method.

In this machine shop, which was converted to group technology in 1954, the labour productivity has risen in 8 years by 240 per cent, and the gross output by 270 per cent; it must be pointed out that at no time during this period has the shop acquired extra floorspace, and hardly any of the machines have been replaced.

The excellent performance of the shop has served as a graphic example and made the job of introducing group production in other shops at the plant easier. Figs 12.2, 12.3 and 12.4 show the results achieved. Eighty per cent of all the components made in this shop are now group machined.

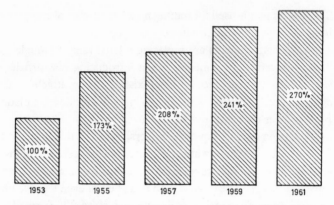

*Fig. 12.2* Graph showing the increase in labour productivity in the machine shop

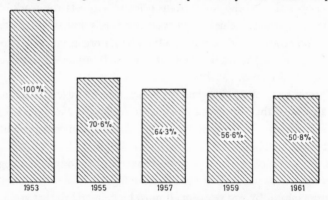

*Fig. 12.3* Graph showing the reduction in machining labour costs in the machine shop

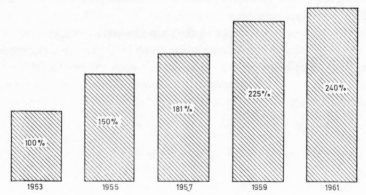

*Fig. 12.4* Graph showing the increase in output from the machine shop

# 13

# the organization of
# labour planning and rate-fixing
# in group production conditions

MATTERS OF planning, especially within shops, are always of major and decisive importance under any conditions. Experience indicates that very often failures to supply components to assembly shops on time are a result of inaccuracies or delays in issuing the planning schedules. Under group production conditions planning is extremely important because an incorrectly compiled schedule can upset the entire group production sequence inside the shop.

Some production workers who are acquainted with the adoption of group techniques will ask whether this method be adopted at plants, where so-called component deficits exist, i.e. where insufficient components are sent for assembly in the current month. The answer is that it not only can but ought to be adopted, because planning and organization in group technology help to reduce component deficits.

The machine that has already been changed over to group technology can once again be quoted as an example. At one time it was one of the worst offenders; the assembly shop it served was often as many as 1500 components short in the month, and had to procure them 'under the counter'. The situation has now been radically altered. The deficit has been greatly reduced and components are now delivered on time for assembly. Admittedly, for the first few months after adopting group technology some components in short supply, scattered among the various groups, were still delivered late. But even by that time a stock was being built up, and the backlog was rapidly reduced in subsequent months.

Difficulties are bound to arise at first when group machining techniques are adopted, but they can be surmounted. For instance, planning principles should be re-examined. This problem could be approached by assigning experienced planners to one shop for 3–4 months to study the conditions there and amend the existing planning methods as appropriate. Proposals to change component planning systems should be discussed in detail with staffs and form the basis of the first trial plans.

The production of components by group machining techniques is organized as follows.

1 Each machine operating by this method handles only the group of components allocated to it, which are made by a given group production sequence.
2 Machining takes place when each machine has been provided with all of the tooling required to make any component in the group allocated to it; this tooling remains with the machine for the whole time it is operating on the group sequence concerned.
3 Most of the resetting is done by the shop-floor operators assigned to the machines.

Under these production conditions one can add to the basic operational planning tasks that ensure that the machines are fully loaded by the components of the groups allocated to them throughout the planning period. This requires highly accurate planning of the work in production sections, and so the matter must be settled during the inter- and intra-shop operational planning of production. Provision must be made in the inter-shop and overall production plans for maintaining full loads on the machines throughout the planning period and also for supplying the rough components in good time. The following preparatory work is carried out with this end in view.

1 Estimate the loads on the equipment in the rough component and machine-shops over the quarter in accordance with the programme for the year.
2 Estimate the loads on the equipment for each group sequence in accordance with the annual programme, by the quarter.
3 Draw up for each shop a schedule for the distribution of the loads on the equipment by group sequences over the entire year.

4 Draw up an operating schedule for each machine, based on the group sequences and covering the entire year.

These jobs must be done before the plant production plan can be formulated. It is drawn up in the following order.

1 Quarterly output schedules are compiled for every stage of production based on the data in the annual programme for the plant, the programme estimate of the loads on the equipment and the planned norm overfulfilment factor.*

2 These schedules are used to draw up for each shop a quarterly (with a monthly breakdown) operational programme for the saleable and gross output by items and numbers off, which also specify the 10-day delivery periods for the products.

Every machine can be kept fully loaded throughout the period of operation on group technology principles, by applying two concepts. The component groups capable of keeping the machines fully and continuously loaded for a year on a given group sequence are included bodily in the machine-shop schedule, to form the basis of the output schedule of the shop for the planning period.

Other groups do not represent full loads throughout the planning period; for them an equipment loading schedule is drawn up for each group production sequence. This in effect constitutes a series of planning dates for starting up production on these component groups. The planning dates should aim at keeping the machines fully loaded over the scheduled period of operation, on the specific group concerned. To do this the volume of work represented by this load must be determined for each group of components.

When compiling operating programmes for rough component shops it is essential to bear in mind that the machine-shops will require blanks to meet their own schedules for each group.

The monthly loading schedule for each machine is based on the component output targets for the section and the equipment loading plan for each group sequence drawn up during the inter-shop planning.

---

* This factor is the relation between the actual and planned output of a worker and, in some cases, a complete factory. – *Editor*.

The planning of the work in the section is based on the loading schedule for each machine.

Accurate and up-to-date production planning for group machining is an indispensable condition for the successful adoption of this technique in production and the eventual full utilization of its extensive organizational and economic possibilities.

All of this work is done by the works production planning section (PPS) with the assistance of representatives from the shops concerned, the calculations being carried out in the data-processing section in a prescribed sequence.

The first job is to estimate for each group production sequence the load of components in the group on the equipment in terms of the annual programme. These estimates must be made because if a machine is not kept fully occupied on the components from the groups allocated to it other work must be planned for it, which may disrupt the group sequence.

The complete estimate is made on the basis of the list (Table 13.1) drawn up by the group technology office serving the Association. After completing the section containing the identification numbers for the equipment groups, and also columns 1–8, the office sends the list to the Association PPS for the next calculations. The right-hand side of the list (columns, 9, 11, 13, 15 and 17) is completed as the calculations are made by the PPS staff, the data being entered at the top of each line in accordance with the annual programme. Columns 10, 12, 14, 16 and 18 are filled in by the data-processing section, which uses the calculated data to produce tabulation No. 1 (Table 13.2). This contains data on the loading of the group technology equipment in terms of the annual programme and quarterly breakdowns. The PPS staff use this chart to draw up a schedule of load distributions on the group production equipment.

By analysing the information in Table 13.3 it is possible to determine the percentage loading on the equipment carrying out a given group production sequence throughout the year.

Next, still on the basis of the data in Table 13.3, a schedule can be drawn up for each shop showing the annual operation of the machines on group production sequences (Table 13.4). The job of compiling this schedule is the most complicated and important stage in inter-shop planning, as it is vital to a successful solution of the problem of main-

Table 13.1 LIST OF COMPONENTS MACHINED BY GROUP SEQUENCE No. 10001

Pro forma No. SO-2  Equipment  Symbol PVS-160 RG-41 RG-42¾T-37

Standard two-shift loading at 20% above rate (in standard hours)  Gp No 15502  02102  02103  01503

| Item | Product | Compo-nent | Machine shop | Opera-tion | Equip-ment group | Section | Piece time (min) | Year No. | Equipment loading | | | | | | | | |
| | | | | | | | | | Hrs | 1st qr No. | Hrs | 2nd qr No. | Hrs | 3rd qr No. | Hrs | 4th qr No. | Hrs |
| 1 | 2 | 3 | 4 | 5 | 6 | 7 | 8 | 9 | 10 | 11 | 12 | 13 | 14 | 15 | 16 | 17 | 18 |
| I | OS-4 | 10 | 5 | 1 | 15502 | I | 1.8 | 1220 | 20.3 | 350<br>400 | 5.9<br>6.6 | 200 | 3.3 | 470 | 7.8 | 200 | 3.3 |
| I | OS-4 | 10 | 3 | 5 | 02102 | I | 2.7 | 1220 | 54.9 | 350<br>400 | 15.8<br>18.0 | 200 | 9.0 | 470 | 21.1 | 200 | 9.0 |
| I | OS-4 | 10 | 3 | 6 | 02102 | I | 1.4 | 1220 | 28.5 | 350<br>400 | 8.2<br>9.3 | 200 | 4.7 | 470 | 10.9 | 200 | 4.7 |
| I | OS-4 | 10 | 3 | 7 | 02103 | I | 4.3 | 1220 | 87.4 | 350<br>400 | 25.1<br>28.6 | 200 | 14.3 | 470 | 33.7 | 200 | 14.3 |
| I | OS-4 | 10 | 3 | 8 | 02103 | I | 2.0 | 1220 | 40.8 | 350<br>400 | 11.7<br>13.3 | 200 | 6.7 | 470 | 15.7 | 200 | 6.7 |
| I | OS-4 | 10 | 3 | 9 | 02103 | I | 3.3 | 1220 | 67.2 | 350<br>400 | 19.3<br>22.0 | 200 | 11.0 | 470 | 25.9 | 200 | 11.0 |
| I | OS-4 | 10 | 3 | 10 | 01503 | I | 1.4 | 1220 | 28.5 | 350<br>400 | 8.2<br>9.3 | 200 | 4.7 | 470 | 10.9 | 200 | 4.7 |
| 2 | OS-6 | 10 | 5 | 1 | 15502 | I | 1.0 | 105 | 1.8 | 25<br>65 | 0.4<br>1.0 | 40 | 0.7 | — | — | 40 | 0.7 |
| 2 | OS-6 | 10 | 3 | 5 | 02102 | I | 3.2 | 105 | 5.7 | 25<br>65 | 1.3<br>3.4 | 40 | 2.2 | — | — | 40 | 2.2 |
| 2 | OS-6 | 10 | 3 | 6 | 02102 | I | 4.6 | 105 | 7.9 | 25<br>65 | 1.9<br>4.9 | 40 | 3.0 | — | — | 40 | 3.0 |
| 2 | OS-6 | 10 | 3 | 7 | 02103 | I | 2.1 | 105 | 3.7 | 25<br>65 | 0.9<br>2.2 | 40 | 1.4 | — | — | 40 | 1.4 |
| 2 | OS-6 | 10 | 3 | 8 | 02103 | I | 2.4 | 105 | 4.2 | 25<br>65 | 1.0<br>2.6 | 40 | 1.6 | — | — | 40 | 1.6 |
| 2 | OS-6 | 10 | 3 | 9 | 02103 | I | 1.4 | 105 | 2.5 | 25<br>65 | 0.7<br>1.5 | 40 | 0.9 | — | — | 40 | 0.9 |

Table 13.2 TABULATION No. 1
Equipment loading, group sequence No. 10001

| Year | Sequence | Machine shop | Sec- tion | Posi- tion | Opera- tion | Equip- ment | Standard hours quarters | | | | Total |
|---|---|---|---|---|---|---|---|---|---|---|---|
| | | | | | | | I | II | III | IV | |
| 9 | 10001 | 3 | 1 | 001 | 05 | 02102 | 15 | 9 | 21 | 9 | |
| 9 | 10001 | 3 | 1 | 001 | 06 | 02102 | 8 | 4 | 10 | 4 | |
| 9 | 10001 | 3 | 1 | 002 | 05 | 02102 | 1 | 2 | | 2 | |
| 9 | 10001 | 3 | 1 | 002 | 06 | 02102 | 2 | 3 | | 3 | |
| 9 | 10001 | 3 | 1 | 004 | 05 | 02102 | 400 | 400 | 400 | 400 | |
| 9 | 10001 | 3 | 1 | 004 | 06 | 02102 | 300 | 280 | 350 | 320 | |
| 9 | 10001 | 3 | 1 | 006 | 05 | 02102 | 150 | 150 | 120 | 130 | |
| 9 | 10001 | 3 | 1 | 006 | 06 | 02102 | 320 | 300 | 380 | 310 | |
| | | | | | | | 1196 | 1198 | 1281 | 1178 | 4853 |
| 9 | 10001 | 3 | 1 | 001 | 07 | 02103 | 25 | 14 | 33 | 14 | |
| 9 | 10001 | 3 | 1 | 001 | 08 | 02103 | 11 | 6 | 15 | 6 | |
| 9 | 10001 | 3 | 1 | 001 | 09 | 02103 | 19 | 11 | 25 | 11 | |
| 9 | 10001 | 3 | 1 | 002 | 07 | 02103 | 0.9 | 1 | | 1 | |
| 9 | 10001 | 3 | 1 | 002 | 08 | 02103 | 1 | 1 | | 1 | |
| 9 | 10001 | 3 | 1 | 002 | 09 | 02103 | 0.7 | 0.9 | | 0.9 | |
| 9 | 10001 | 3 | 1 | 004 | 07 | 02103 | 150 | 180 | 170 | 140 | |
| 9 | 10001 | 3 | 1 | 004 | 08 | 02103 | 110 | 120 | 115 | 100 | |
| 9 | 10001 | 3 | 1 | 004 | 09 | 02103 | 80 | 100 | 90 | 70 | |
| 9 | 10001 | 3 | 1 | 006 | 07 | 02103 | 220 | 200 | 190 | 190 | |
| 9 | 10001 | 3 | 1 | 006 | 08 | 02103 | 180 | 160 | 150 | 150 | |
| 9 | 10001 | 3 | 1 | 006 | 09 | 02103 | 300 | 280 | 270 | 270 | |
| | | | | | | | 1097.6 | 1073.9 | 1058 | 953.9 | 4182.5 |
| 9 | 10001 | 3 | 1 | 001 | 10 | 01503 | 8 | 4 | 10 | 4 | |
| 9 | 10001 | 3 | 1 | 002 | 10 | 01503 | 10 | 12 | | 12 | |
| 9 | 10001 | 3 | 1 | 004 | 10 | 01503 | 60 | 80 | 70 | 50 | |
| 9 | 10001 | 3 | 1 | 006 | 10 | 01503 | 40 | 35 | 30 | 30 | |
| | | | | | | | 118 | 131 | 110 | 96 | 455 |

Table 13.3 SCHEDULE
Load distributions on the equipment operating group sequences, for Machine Shop No. 3, in accordance with the annual programme (in months, to the nearest third month)

| Section No. | Sequence No. | Equip- ment code | Machine stock No. | Loading by quarters and months 1st qr  2nd qr  3rd qr  4th qr I  II  III  IV  V  VI  VII  VIII  IX  X  XI  XII |
|---|---|---|---|---|
| 1 | 10001 | RG–41 | 25 | |
| 1 | 20121 | RG–41 | 31 | |
| 1 | 20148 | RG–41 | 36 | |
| 1 | 20149 | RG–41 | 38 | |
| 1 | 20151 | RG–41 | 39 | |
| 1 | 10001 | RG–42 | 26 | |
| 1 | 20155 | RG–42 | 28 | |
| 1 | 20157 | RG–42 | 29 | |
| 1 | 20159 | RG–42 | 30 | |
| 1 | 20162 | RG–42 | 32 | |

Table 13.4 SCHEDULE
The annual operation of machines in Machine Shop No. 3 on group sequences

Approved
Production manager

| Section No. | Equip-ment code | Machine stock No. | Group sequence loadings |
|---|---|---|---|
| | | | 1st qr: I II III   2nd qr: IV V VI   3rd qr: VII VIII IX   4th qr: X XI XII |
| I | RG–41 | 25 | ▬▬▬▬▬▬▬▬▬ 10001 ▬▬▬▬▬▬▬ |
| I | RG–41 | 31 | ▬▬▬▬ 20121 ▬▬▬▬▬ 20151   Any compts |
| I | RG–41 | 36 | ▬▬▬▬▬ ▬20148 ▬▬▬▬▬ |
| I | RG–41 | 38 | Any compts ▬▬▬ 20149 ▬▬▬   Any components |
| I | RG–41 | 40 | ▬▬▬▬▬ 20152 ▬▬▬▬ |
| I | RG–42 | 26 | ▬▬▬▬▬▬ 10001 ▬▬▬▬▬ |
| I | RG–42 | 28 | ▬ 20162 ▬ ▬ 20155 ▬ ▬▬▬ Any components |
| I | RG–42 | 29 | ▬ 20157 ▬ 20159 ▬▬▬ Any components |

Agreed:                                              Head of scheduling
Manager, Machine Shop No. 3                          office:

taining full loads on the machines throughout the period they are operating on the group production sequence concerned. The job is therefore carried out in collaboration with the shop staff.

One copy of the schedule goes to the shop where it is used to establish the dates on which the machines are to be occupied on the group production sequences allocated to them, and also the period they are to be used for machining components in individual production sequences.

The plant PPS uses the schedule as a basic document for planning the volumes of work required to keep the machines fully occupied with components in the groups allocated to them for the operating periods indicated by the schedule. These volumes of work, as mentioned above, need only be found for groups of components that will not keep the machines fully and continuously loaded throughout the year. The estimated work volumes are entered at the bottom of each line in the list (Table 13.1). The PPS inserts in columns 11, 13, 15 and 17 the number of components to be included in the quarterly equipment loading plan, and in columns 12, 14, 16 and 18 the volumes of work in standard hours. The data-processing section processes this information to produce tabulation No. 2, which takes the form of a quarterly equipment loading plan for the group production sequence concerned (Table 13.5) and contains for each planning entry the list of components in the group (see Table 13.2), the volume of work for the quarter and the total load on the equipment during this period as given by the operating schedule (see Table 13.4). A typical example is given in Table 13.5 for component group No. 20157.

Table 13.5 TABULATION No. 2

Quarterly equipment loading plan for group sequence No. 20157 in Machine shop No. 3

| Sequence No. | Section No. | Position No. | Operation No. | Equip-ment | Piece time (min.) whole | tenths | No. of components | Standard hours |
|---|---|---|---|---|---|---|---|---|
| 20157 | I | I | 2 | 02103 | 2 | 7 | 530 | 24 |
| 20157 | I | 4 | 2 | 02103 | I | 4 | 530 | 12 |
| 20157 | I | 6 | 2 | 02103 | 3 | 2 | 56 | 3 |
| 20157 | I | 8 | 2 | 02103 | 4 | 6 | 56 | 4 |
| 20157 | I | 10 | 2 | 02103 | 3 | 8 | 3900 | 247 |
| 20157 | I | 11 | 2 | 02103 | 4 | 7 | 4000 | 313 |
| 20157 | I | 12 | 2 | 02103 | 4 | 2 | 4500 | 315 |
| 20157 | I | 16 | 2 | 02103 | 5 | I | 6200 | 527 |
| | | | | | | | | 1445 |

The quarterly equipment loading plan for each group production sequence (Table 13.5) constitutes a supplement to the shop quarterly saleable output plan. In a number of the group entries the planned number of components exceeds the number included in the shop saleable output plan. In this case the volumes of work required to keep the equipment fully occupied are noted.

Hence the quarterly equipment loading plan for each group of components (Table 13.5) does in fact, as stated above, constitute a series of starting dates for the production of these components. Under no circumstances should it be used as a component output plan, otherwise certain items of equipment would be systematically but quite unjustifiably overloaded.

The shop uses this plan to draw up the monthly machine loading schedules, and the production planning department uses it to draw up the operational programmes.

The entire operation of drawing up monthly, quarterly and annual schedules may seem awkward and difficult. But experience proves that if suitable preparations are made and all of the forms and order of filling them in are discussed beforehand with the persons doing the job, the task becomes perfectly feasible and has the effect of disciplining and systematizing the entire production process from the initial phase, i.e. from the supply of materials right up to the delivery of the finished products to the stores.

The adoption of group technology in production has paved the way for the introduction of progressive rate-fixing methods. Practice indicates that higher labour productivities are achieved by using technically based (basic) rather than experimental-statistical rates. At many plants, however, technically based rates are only used in medium- or large-batch production.

The technical rate-fixing system employed at the majority of plants for individual production sequences is based on the necessity for calculating the rate for each operation element by element. It takes up a great deal of the time of highly skilled engineers and technicians. The high labour costs of technical rate-fixing are the chief reason why so comparatively few basic rates are used in medium- and small-batch plants. Practice confirms that in these conditions (high diversification and comparatively frequent product changes) it is virtually impossible to adopt basic rates on a large scale for individual production sequences.

The attempt to reduce the labour costs of technical rate-fixing by working out and using consolidated rates without employing group production principles did not achieve popularity. The unavoidable errors in the rates are not conducive to the required accuracy in the estimated rates. A group rate-fixing system based on the group machining technique can provide the answer to the problem of maximizing the coverage of components with technically based (basic) or estimated basic rates.

The guiding principle of the group rate-fixing system is that the basic piece time is determined for typical representatives of the production group rather than for each separate component. The piece times for the rest of the components in the group are based on those for the representative component, using one of the following methods: operation-by-operation interpolation, consolidated interpolation, visual comparison or graphical analysis. They all reduce the rate-fixing labour costs appreciably.*

---

* Each of these methods is discussed at length in the pamphlet by V. L. Mantsevich 'Rapid rate-fixing methods for jobbing and small-batch production'. Sudprongiz, 1957.

Table 13.6 RATE-FIXING CARD FOR A GROUP SEQUENCE

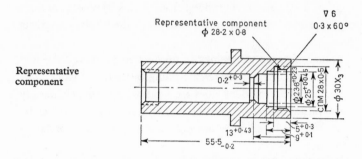

| Operation on rep. | Details | Machining dia. | Length (mm) | Machining conditions Speed rev/min | Depth | Feed | No. of passes |
|---|---|---|---|---|---|---|---|
| 1 | Set up and remove | | | | | | |
| 2 | Rough turn 23.8 dia. | 23.8 | 13+2 | 1740 | 0.5 | 0.13 | 1 |
| 3 | Rough turn 25 dia. | 25 | 9+2 | 1740 | 1.3 | 0.13 | 1 |
| 4 | Turn for thread | 24 | 5+2 | 1740 | 2 | 0.13 | 1 |
| 4a | Turn groove | 28.2 | 0.1+2 | 1740 | 0.8 | 0.06 | 1 |
| 4b | Remove burr 0.3 × 60 | 28 | | | | | |
| 5 | Face end, 55.5 dia. | 30 | 2+2 | 1740 | 0.5 | 0.06 | 1 |
| 6 | Finish turn 23.8 dia. | 23.8 | 4+2 | 1740 | 1.4 | 0.13 | 1 |
| 7 | Remove burr | 23.8 | | | | | |
| 8 | Turn dia. 25A₃ | 25 | 4+2 | 1740 | 0.5 | 0.06 | 1 |
| 9 | Cut thread SPM28 × 0.5 | 28 | 5+2 | 915 | | 0.5 | 6 |
| 10 | Remove sharp corners | | | | | | |
| 11 | Inspect total | | | | | | |

An understanding of the group rate-fixing method can be obtained by considering an example in which the piece time is calculated for a component in one of the groups (Table 13.6).

The left-hand side of the card contains the piece calculation for the representative component, found by adding up the operation times, while the right-hand side contains the piece time calculation for another component in the group, found by the technique of operation-by-operation interpolation. Each working operation (pass) determines the coefficient of proportionality and is used to calculate the machining time. The auxiliary time is assumed to be the same as for the representative component.

This method of fixing the piece times for components provides the most accurate results and cuts the rate-fixing labour costs by 30–40 per cent. The piece times found for components in a production group

Table 13.6 (*Continued*)    ▽6

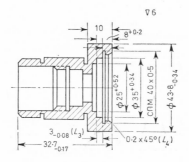

| Time T (min.) | | | | Operations on compt | Basic dimensions (mm) | | | | | Pro- portion- ality factor | Time T (min.) | | | |
|---|---|---|---|---|---|---|---|---|---|---|---|---|---|---|
| M/c | Aux. | Sur- plus | Piece | and rep. | 1 | 2 | 3 | 4 | 5 | | M/c | Aux. | Sur- plus | Piece |
| | 0.24 | | | 1/1 | | | | | | | | 0.24 | | |
| 0.07 | 0.1 | | | 2/5 | | | | | | 1 | 0.03 | 0.18 | | |
| 0.05 | 0.1 | | | 3/2 | 10+2 | | | | | 0.8 | 0.06 | 0.1 | | |
| 0.03 | 0.1 | | | 4/3 | | 8+2 | | | | 0.9 | 0.04 | 0.1 | | |
| 0.02 | — | | | 5/4 | | | 6+2 | | | 1.1 | 0.03 | 0.1 | | |
| 0.09 | — | | | 6/4 | | | | | | 1 | 0.03 | 0.1 | | |
| 0.03 | 0.18 | | | 6a/4a | | | | | | 1 | 0.02 | | | |
| 0.03 | 0.1 | | | 6b/4b | | | | | | 1 | 0.09 | | | |
| 0.09 | — | | | 7/5 | | | | 5+2 | | 1.8 | 0.06 | 0.1 | | |
| 0.06 | 0.1 | | | 8/10 | | | | | | 1 | 0.11 | | | |
| 0.09 | 0.56 | | | 9/9 | | | | | 5+2 | 1 | 0.09 | 0.56 | | |
| 0.11 | 0.67 | | | 10/11 | | | | | | 1 | | 0.67 | | |
| 0.67 | 2.15 | 0.16 | 2.98 | | | | | | | | 0.56 | 2.15 | 0.16 | 2.87 |

by the group rate-fixing approach compare closely with the basic rates, and there are no contradictions as is the case when rates are fixed individually.

Fig. 13.1 compares the rates fixed by the normal technical rate-fixing procedure and those fixed by the group method. The representative component of the group concerned is No. 48. It can be seen from the graph that the rates fixed by the group method show much less scatter than those found by individual rate-fixing.

Various nomograms are often used in group rate-fixing to curtail and simplify the piece time calculations. Fig. 13.2 is a nomogram for determining the basic time for milling plane surfaces as a function of the length and width of machining. By using these nomograms and the group rate-fixing method, rate-fixers can substantially curtail the time spent on such calculations. For individual production sequences an

G

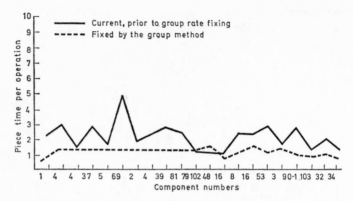

*Fig. 13.1* Comparative diagram showing the current rates and those established by the group method

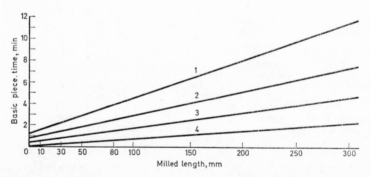

*Fig. 13.2* Nomogram for milling times using cutter heads, as a function of the length and width of the surface;
milled widths 1 – 200 mm; 2 – 180 mm; 3 – 100 mm; 4 – 50 mm

experienced rate-fixer can calculate 10–12 operations per day, whereas for group production sequences he can calculate 25–30 operations, using the rate-fixing system adopted at the Association plants. This means that the use of technically based piece times can be extended and the number of so-called 'profitable' and 'unprofitable' jobs in production reduced.

# 14

# the provision of supplies
# for group production

SUPPLY PROBLEMS play a decisive, perhaps even the main, role in plants operating on group principles. It can be seen on examining the ordinary production planning schedules drawn up by every plant that as a rule very little time is set aside on them for the provision of material supplies.

Too little attention has been devoted in the past and is being devoted at present by the enterprises to organizing the supply of materials. Quite obviously supply departments should be run by competent engineers with a knowledge of production economics and organization. Supplies of materials must be organized on a scientific basis.

In present-day conditions the standard stocks of various grades and sizes of material must be based on the production processes employed at the plants. The determining factor in fixing stock levels must be the saleable output taking into account the normal levels of work in progress for each individual item, for the year, quarter and month.

The material-supply situation acquires especial significance in group production conditions since the equipment is loaded strictly in accordance with the component groups allocated to the machines. Experience has shown that a 10-day stock of blanks is required to keep a machine going without interruptions. Supply holdups cannot be tolerated in these circumstances since they result in components being transferred from one machine to another, large-scale retooling and on occasion the abandonment of group techniques. Shops operating on group principles must be regarded as conveyor belts, on which the absence of a single component will disrupt the entire operation.

Under such conditions the planning and day-to-day organization of material supplies must be of a consistently high standard. This chapter considers the materials and machinery supply system adopted at several plants within the Association. It has already been adopted at other plants using group production methods.

The production programme for the shops is planned in product sets; targets are fixed by the quarter, with monthly breakdowns. A product set is defined as the complete set of components made in a given shop by the operational production sequence and component routing in use. The supply of materials and blanks is planned to allow for the standard anticipation of the production target schedule in the shop to be supplied.

The proposed material planning system, besides safeguarding the supply of materials for production, also provides an early warning of any difficulties that may arise in the supply of materials or blanks to specific sectors of production. Such a system demands a high technical level within the plant, covering the entire output, together with quite strict production discipline. The system adopted to introduce modification in the drawings and production techniques should be strictly regulated.

It is essential under these conditions to make the rough components within the plant, in a shop which should be placed under the control of the deputy commercial director of the plant. The cutting out of any material can be organized, and roughing work and other preparatory operations concentrated in the rough-component shop. A small material planning section should be set up in the shop and given the following duties.

1 Drawing up the basic and auxiliary material estimates (needed to fulfil the production programme) to justify the specified materials orders submitted to the council of the national economy by the supply department.

2 Estimating the detailed programme of the rough-component shop and the materials required in the planning period.

3 Estimating the materials that will bypass the rough-component shop and go straight to the production shops from the stores (charge materials, timber, textiles, etc.).

4 Estimating the normal stocks of materials in the supply department stores.

The material planning and production supply system is based on the material consumption rates and centralized supply of blanks to the production shops. The basic consumption rates required in production are as follows.

1  The standard consumption of basic material per component, which is calculated from the job card for the rough component (Table 14.1, page 90);
2  The standard consumption of auxiliary material per unit of output (Table 14.2, page 91);
3  The cumulative standard consumptions of materials per unit of output in specified form by grades and sizes (Table 14.3, page 91).

These rates are drawn up in the chief production engineer's department and sent to the rough-component shop. Changes in the rates are made official by appropriate notifications and should be conveyed without delay to the component shop.

The material planning is done in the following sequence. Four months before the planning period (quarter) commences the scheduling section in the works PPS draws up the material supplies schedule for the quarter. After approval by the deputy commercial director, the schedule is forwarded to the rough-component shop planning office. The schedule is then broken down for each stage of production in respect of standard batch sizes, duration of the production cycle at each stage and the standard lead times for the product.

Table 14.4 (page 92) give an example of the calculation of a schedule for supplying machine shops with basic materials.

The schedule for supplying components to the foundry, drop forging, woodworking, finishing, assembly and other shops are drawn up in the same form. Schedules are also drawn up for outside supplies to be obtained from the Association co-operation department.

The rough-component shop planning section uses the information in the schedule (Table 14.4) and standard material consumptions indicated above (see Tables 14.2 and 14.3) to estimate the material requirements for the planning period. A list of the materials required in specified form for each grade and size (Table 14.5, page 92) is dispatched to the supply department three and a half months before the planning

Table 14.1 JOB CARD FOR ROUGH COMPONENT CUTTING

| | No. of blanks | No. off per blank | No. in product | Symbol | Component | Operation | Machine shop No. 5 |
|---|---|---|---|---|---|---|---|
| | 1 | 1 | 1 | A-3-1 | 20-16 | 1 | |

| Material | Size | Weight | No. off per bar | Standard unit consumption | Blank wt or size | Rough wt or size | Finished wt or size |
|---|---|---|---|---|---|---|---|
| Brass LS-59-1 GOST 2060-48 | dia. 35 length 3500 | 28.550 | 27 | 1.057 | 0.978 | 0.978 | 0.643 |

| Substitute materials allowed on drawing | Blank wt: or size | Waste usable for components |
|---|---|---|

| Production sequence | Equipment | Attachment | Cutting tool | Gauge |
|---|---|---|---|---|
| 1. Trim bar end, 20 mm | DP-35-1 | | | |
| 2. Cut 121 mm lengths | " | | | |
| 3. Subsequent machining on lathe | | | | |

Diagram labels: φ35 · 20 · 127 · 121 · 3 · 3500 mm · Discard 51 mm

Table 14.2 STANDARD CONSUMPTIONS OF AUXILIARY
MATERIAL

| Material group | Material | GOST |
|---|---|---|
| No. 6 | Grade B–70 aviation spirit | 1012–56 |

| Instrument | Standard consumptions (litres) per shop | | | | | | | Mods (date & signature) |
|---|---|---|---|---|---|---|---|---|
| | No. 3 | No. 6 | No. 7 | No. 10 | No. 14 | No. 17 | Total | |
| MZ | 2.6 | 1.54 | 3.2 | 7.9 | 0.01 | 3.9 | 19.15 | |
| KM | 1.4 | 1.4 | 1.4 | 2.7 | 0.01 | 0.57 | 7.48 | |
| OM–618 | 0.2 | 1.1 | 0.65 | 0.234 | — | 0.62 | 2.804 | |
| PP–2 | 1.4 | 2.2 | 1.7 | 3.1 | 0.01 | 0.64 | 9.05 | |
| PP–4 | 1.4 | 1.9 | 1.5 | 3.1 | 0.01 | 0.8 | 8.71 | |
| AL–23 | 1.5 | 1.9 | 1.9 | 3.1 | 0.01 | 0.7 | 9.11 | |
| V–56 | 0.2 | 0.08 | 0.5 | 0.3 | — | 0.16 | 1.24 | |
| K–2P | 0.1 | 0.05 | 0.3 | 0.3 | — | 0.27 | 1.02 | |

Table 14.3 CUMULATIVE STANDARD CONSUMPTIONS OF
MATERIALS IN THE PRODUCTS, BY GRADES AND SIZES

| Material grade | Section | Size (mm) | Units | Products | | | | | | | | |
|---|---|---|---|---|---|---|---|---|---|---|---|---|
| | | | | BR–1 | BR–3 | BI–6 | BI–8 | IM–7 | IM–8 | UF–5 | P–1 | RL–1 |
| Brass LS–59–1 | Round bar | 6 | kg | 0.112 | — | 0.415 | 0.220 | — | — | 0.040 | — | 0.064 |
| 1 | | 8 | kg | — | — | — | — | 1.010 | 1.300 | — | — | — |
| | | 10 | kg | — | — | 0.856 | 0.920 | — | — | 0.235 | — | — |
| | | 12 | kg | 0.468 | 0.482 | — | — | 1.318 | 0.865 | — | — | 0.018 |
| | | 16 | kg | — | — | 1.440 | 1.650 | — | — | — | — | — |
| | | 20 | kg | 0.917 | 0.975 | 1.860 | 1.972 | — | — | — | 0.372 | — |
| | | 22 | kg | — | — | — | — | 0.318 | — | 0.417 | — | — |
| | | 25 | kg | 0.162 | — | 1.298 | 2.312 | 1.124 | 0.719 | 1.084 | — | — |
| | | 28 | kg | — | — | — | — | — | 1.248 | — | — | 0.364 |
| | | 30 | kg | 1.568 | 1.782 | 2.018 | 1.241 | 1.684 | — | 2.417 | — | 0.728 |
| | | 35 | kg | — | — | — | 0.918 | — | 1.012 | — | 2.861 | — |
| | | 38 | kg | — | — | — | — | 0.469 | — | — | — | — |
| | | 40 | kg | — | 1.190 | 1.278 | 0.832 | — | 1.419 | 1.768 | 1.412 | — |
| | | 50 | kg | 0.817 | 0.655 | 0.812 | 0.958 | 1.247 | — | 2.482 | — | — |
| | | 55 | kg | — | — | — | 1.035 | 0.623 | 1.012 | — | 1.721 | — |

period commences. The supply department draws up specified material requisitions based on the information in the list and taking into account the forecast of stocks of materials remaining in the plant stores at the start of the planning quarter. The drawing-up of these requisitions completes the first stage of materials planning. In the second stage the rough-component shop programme is worked out for each separate component, and the materials that the shop will need for the planning period (quarter) are calculated.

Table 14.4
Approved
Deputy Commercial Director
..............................196  .

### SCHEDULE
of Basic Materials Supplies, IIIrd quarter 196  .
(in sets required by rough-component shops)

| Product symbol | Finished products output plan | | | Planned stock July 1st | Planned monthly provision | | | Total | Planned stock Oct 1st |
|---|---|---|---|---|---|---|---|---|---|
| | IIIrd qr | IVth qr | Total | | VII | VIII | IX | | |
| BI–3 | 300 | 400 | 700 | 200 | 100 | 150 | 150 | 400 | 300 |
| BI–4 | 750 | 750 | 1500 | 500 | 250 | 250 | 250 | 750 | 500 |
| KS–1 | 150 | 200 | 350 | 150 | — | 150 | 100 | 250 | 250 |
| OL–2 | 450 | 450 | 900 | 300 | 150 | 150 | 150 | 450 | 300 |
| R–1 | 4500 | 4500 | 9000 | 3000 | 1500 | 1500 | 2000 | 5000 | 3500 |
| UF–5 | 15 | 20 | 35 | 15 | 30 | — | — | 30 | 30 |

Table 14.5 LIST OF MATERIAL REQUIREMENTS FOR
YEAR 196  , QUARTER......

| Material grade | Section | Size | Units | Quantity |
|---|---|---|---|---|
| Brass LS–59–1 | Round bar | 6 | Tonne | 0.040 |
| ,, | ,, | 8 | ,, | 0.187 |
| ,, | ,, | 10 | ,, | 0.500 |
| ,, | ,, | 12 | ,, | 0.850 |
| ,, | ,, | 20 | ,, | 1.545 |
| ,, | ,, | 25 | ,, | 0.850 |
| ,, | ,, | 30 | ,, | 1.950 |
| ,, | ,, | 35 | ,, | 0.840 |
| ,, | ,, | 38 | ,, | 0.230 |
| ,, | ,, | 40 | ,, | 0.750 |
| ,, | ,, | 50 | ,, | 0.245 |
| ,, | ,, | 55 | ,, | 0.380 |
| ,, | ,, | 60 | ,, | 0.150 |
| ,, | ,, | 65 | ,, | 0.120 |
| ,, | ,, | 70 | ,, | 1.640 |
| ,, | ,, | 100 | ,, | 0.840 |

The component programme is drawn up 45 days before the start of
the quarter by the scheduling section of the plant PPS. The programme
is calculated for each component of the end product using the planning
and record card shown in Table 14.6. The number of components for
which materials are required is determined in the light of the information obtained from the supplies schedule (see Table 14.4), the uses made
of the component in other products and the work in progress. If the
component comes into a production group for which an equipment

Table 14.6 PLANNING AND RECORD CARD No............

| Symbol | BI-3 | Rough component | Component: Clutch component No. 51-10 | Group sequence | |
|---|---|---|---|---|---|
| Order | 01045 | Plastics | Signal to order scrap.........off | Symbol | No. |
| Route | 5-1-7 | Pressure diecasting | | BI-3 | 1 |
| | | Liquid-metal stamping | Given stock of .......... off | BI-6 | 1 |
| | | Precision casting | | L-1 | 1 |
| | | Sand casting | Issued to assembly No........ | KU-1 | 1 |
| | | Shell casting | Components per set, ........... off | | |
| | | Automatics | | | |
| | | Pressing | | | |

| Piece time (min) | Route | Stock on 1/IV plan | Stock on 1/IV actual | Shortage (−) Surplus (+) | Plan qr II | Total | Including, months IV | V | VI |
|---|---|---|---|---|---|---|---|---|---|
| 0.83 | 5 | 350 | | | 350 | | 120 | 130 | 100 |
| 10.9 | 1 | 190 | | | 300 | | | 150 | 150 |
| 1.5 | 7 | 55 | | | 270 | | 90 | 90 | 90 |

SHOP NO. 5

| Date | No. | Total |
|---|---|---|
| 10/IV | 250 | 250 |

SHOP NO. 1

| Date | No. | Total | Stock |
|---|---|---|---|
| 1/III | | | 250 |
| 25/IV | 50 | 50 | 200 |

SHOP NO. 7

| Date | No. | Total | Stock |
|---|---|---|---|
| 1/III | | | 168 |
| 12/IV | 100 | 100 | 68 |
| | | | 118 |

SHOP NO. 16

| Date | No. | Total | Stock |
|---|---|---|---|
| 1/III | | 85 | 285 |
| 1/IV | | | 200 |

loading plan has been drawn up, the number off is found directly from the plan (see Table 13.5).

In the example given in Table 14.6, shop No. 5 is the rough-component shop. The planned stocks for each shop are shown here as a running total. This means that shop No. 5 should have built up a stock of 350 components, which at 1st of April should constitute the work in hand in the shops following shop No. 5 in the production route.

The work each shop has in hand on a particular component can be found by subtracting the planned stock in the shop doing the supplying from that in the shop it supplies. For instance, shop No. 1 will, according to the plan, have 160 (350−190) items in progress and shop No. 7 will have 135 (190−55).

The calculation of the carry-over stocks is crucial to the normal functioning of the plant, especially in group production conditions. The carry-over stock holds the key to the determination of optimum material stock levels.

After fixing the planning targets on these cards the rough-component shop material planning section enters this information selectively on the shop material planning and record cards.

These cards constitute the basic planning record documents for the shop and are used to calculate the materials that the shop will require for the planning period. Table 14.7 gives an example of how to fill in the card. Along the top are shown the instrument-type number, the component number, the grade of the material, the item number, the shape and size of the production blank, the number of components per blank, the material consumption rate per component and the stores number and routing of the blank through the shop.

The lower part of the card shows the stock situation at stocktaking, the monthly targets during the quarter, the number of blanks and corresponding number of components to be supplied in the planning period (month), and the weight of material required. Notes are kept here of the blanks going into production and entering the shop stores, and their final delivery to the next shop.

The rough-component shop production engineer enters the material consumption rate per component and the size of the production blank on the card, and it is his job also to alter these figures immediately on

Table 14.7 COMPONENT(SHOP) MATERIAL PLANNING
AND RECORD CARD

| Instrument | Compt No. | Grade | Item No. | Section | Thickness | Width | Length | Quant | Units | Wt | Stock | Route |
|---|---|---|---|---|---|---|---|---|---|---|---|---|
| MIM–8m | 55–16 | LS–59 | 5147–0280 | rd bar | 28 | — | 865 | 66 | 2 | 0.069 | 2 | R.P. 1 |

| Month | Stock plan | actual | Make | Wt (kg) | Issued | En route blank shop | lathes | Issues | Notes |
|---|---|---|---|---|---|---|---|---|---|
| At 1/1/62 | 240 | 180 | 66/1 | 4.6 | | | | | |
| I | 50 | | 66/1 | 4.6 | | | | | |
| II | 50 | | 66/1 | 4.6 | | | | | |
| III | 50 | | 66/1 | 4.6 | | | | | |
| | | | total | 18.4 | | | | | |
| IV | 50 | | 66/1 | 4.6 | | | | | |
| V | 50 | | 66/1 | 4.6 | | | | | |
| VI | 50 | | 66/1 | 4.6 | | | | | |
| | | | total | 13.8 | | | | | |
| VII | — | | — | — | | | | | |
| VIII | 65 | | 66/1 | 4.6 | | | | | |
| IX | 65 | | 66/1 | 4.6 | | | | | |
| | | | total | 9.2 | | | | | |

receiving notification of changes in the production documentation. A specific production engineer must be held responsible for this work.

Organization on this basis will ensure that the quotas are maintained at the required level.

The remaining essential elements of the card are filled in by the rough-component shop materials planning section and planning control office. The supplies that the shop will need for the planning period are calculated on machines in the following order.

The first calculation is of the number of material blanks to be supplied to the machine shops in the planning period. It is completed by the materials planning section and takes into account the work in progress at stocktaking and the ratio of blanks to the number of components required in the programme for each month. The results of the calculation are entered in the 'Supply' column, the number of material blanks to be inserted in the denominator and the number of components obtainable from them in the numerator.

The data-processing section can then use the material consumption rates per component and the number of components to be supplied per month (given in the numerator) to calculate the weight of material required. The section then transfers the information from the planning record cards to punched cards in conformity with the punched card system and machine setup in use, sorts all of the punched cards in order of the appropriate criteria and tabulates the information. This work is completed by the issue of two tabulation charts.

Table 14.8 TABULATION CHART No. 1
Materials requirements for 1st quarter 1960, Store No. 2

| Item No. | Units | Dimensions (mm) thickness width whole fractions w. f. | Monthly quantities for months 1 w. f. | 2 w. f. | 3 w. f. | Total for quarter w. f. | Store No. | Card No. |
|---|---|---|---|---|---|---|---|---|
| 32080030 | 2 | 30 | 250 | 250 | 250 | 750 | 2 | 25188 |
| 32080030 | 2 | 30 | 1 | 1 | | 2 | 2 | 01077 |
| 32080030 | 2 | 30 | 20 | 10 | 10 | 40 | 2 | 53165 |
| 32080030 | 2 | 30 | 24 | | | 24 | 2 | 88162 |
| | | | 295 | 261 | 260 | 816 | | |
| 32080040 | 2 | 40 | 100 | 120 | 130 | 350 | 2 | 29193 |
| 32080040 | 2 | 40 | 300 | | 200 | 500 | 2 | 26163 |
| | | | 400 | 120 | 330 | 850 | | |
| 32080050 | 2 | 50 | 50 | | | 50 | 2 | 92202 |
| 32080050 | 2 | 50 | 100 | 100 | 100 | 300 | 2 | 61124 |
| | | | 150 | 100 | 100 | 350 | | |

Number 1 chart (Table 14.8) contains the quarterly material requirements in grades and sizes for the entire output and for each individual component, using the component card numbers as identification. The rough-component shop uses this chart in starting up production on each grade and size of material.

Number 2 tabulation chart (Table 14.9) contains the quarterly materials supply plan by grades and sizes, and by months. This plan is sent to the supply department 30 days before the planning period. If the plan has to be drawn up by hand without mechanical aids the component programme estimate is issued to the rough-component shop 60 days before the start of the planning quarter.

On receiving the quarterly materials supply plan for basic production the plant supply department takes into consideration the materials requirement for other purposes and draws up the overall materials supply plan for the quarter (Table 14.10).

Table 14.9 TABULATION CHART No. 2

Materials supply plan, 1st quarter 1960, Store No. 2

| Material grade | Units | Item No. | Dimensions | | Monthly quantities for months | | | | | | Total for | Store No. |
|---|---|---|---|---|---|---|---|---|---|---|---|---|
| | | | thickness width whole fractions w. | f. | 1 w. | f. | 2 w. | f. | 3 w. | f. | w. f. | |
| LS–59 | 2 | 51470050 | 5 | | 60 | | 60 | | 60 | | 180 | 2 |
| | 2 | 51470060 | 6 | | 2120 | | 1000 | | 1000 | | 4120 | 2 |
| | 2 | 51470070 | 7 | | 160 | | 280 | | 430 | | 870 | 2 |
| | 2 | 51470080 | 8 | | 6942 | | 6591 | | 7552 | | 21085 | 2 |
| | 2 | 51470090 | 9 | | 50 | | | | | | 50 | 2 |
| | 2 | 51470100 | 10 | | 1070 | | 400 | | 420 | | 1890 | 2 |
| | 2 | 51470120 | 12 | | 40 | | 40 | | 40 | | 120 | 2 |
| | 2 | 51470140 | 14 | | 1500 | | 2000 | | 2500 | | 6000 | 2 |
| | 2 | 51470160 | 16 | | 450 | | 350 | | 520 | | 1320 | 2 |
| | 2 | 51470180 | 18 | | 4550 | | 3450 | | 2825 | | 10825 | 2 |
| | 2 | 51470200 | 20 | | 5600 | | 4285 | | 3615 | | 13500 | 2 |
| | 2 | 51470220 | 22 | | 2250 | | 2250 | | 1500 | | 6000 | 2 |

The demand for materials for internal consumption, experimental work and toolroom use, including those required by the transport and housing departments, is determined in the light of the specified material requisitions from the relevant departments submitted to the supply department $3\frac{1}{2}$ months before the planning period.

Table 14.10 shows the form and an example of an overall supply plan for round brass. It indicates the total requirement of each size for the quarter and each month, taking into account changes, shortfall on output during the preceding quarter and the actual issue of material to production.

The progress made in fulfilling the plan is indicated graphically in the middle of the form as follows. The quantity of each size of material available in the stores at the start of the planning period, the shortfall on output during the preceding quarter and the amount of material issued for current production are determined. The amount of material needed to meet the quarterly requirement, taking into account amendments and shortfall on output, is entered in the appropriate column by colouring a proportion of it in yellow or some other light colour. Then as the material is issued for production the coloured part of the column is painted in proportion to the total requirement, using a darker colour.

This method of depicting the supply position very clearly shows the extent of the actual provision of materials and their entry into

Table 14.10 MATERIALS SUPPLY PLAN FOR 2ND QUARTER 196 .

| Grade | | | | | *LS–59–1, round bar* | | | | | | |
|---|---|---|---|---|---|---|---|---|---|---|---|
| Size | 6 | 7 | 8 | 9 | 10 | 12 | 14 | 15 | 16 | 18 | 20 |
| Quantity | 143 | 307 | 193 | 41 | 112 | 554 | 2045 | 449 | 439 | 1936 | 652 |

| Shortage | | | | | | | | | | | |
|---|---|---|---|---|---|---|---|---|---|---|---|
| April | 104 | 258 | 160 | 41 | 78 | 198 | 839 | 213 | 213 | 714 | 303 |
| May | 21 | 29 | 17 | — | 20 | 196 | 674 | 155 | 155 | 645 | 231 |
| June | 18 | 20 | 16 | — | 14 | 160 | 532 | 81 | 71 | 557 | 118 |
| Requirement, amended | 144 | 308 | 194 | — | 113 | 569 | 3106 | — | 446 | 1972 | 695 |
| Issued | 133 | 290 | 162 | 34 | 115 | 741 | 1925 | — | 242 | 1766 | 561 |

production. The admission of materials to the plant and their outgoings from the stores are determined from the daily returns submitted by the stores to the supply department. The 'Amended requirement' and 'Issued' columns are filled in with an ordinary pencil.

The overall supply plan is signed by the deputy commercial director and constitutes the basic planning document on which the entire practical work of the supply department is based. It is used to limit the release of materials from the stores and to check that fresh supplies are procured as the stocks run down.

If accuracy is to be maintained in material planning and the carry-over material stocks are to be kept at the specified level, a strict procedure must be laid down for the rapid detection of spoilage or losses giving rise to unexpected and additional demands for materials.

It is vitally important that every case of spoilage or loss of components or material blanks be detected and notified in good time. Such cases should not escape the attention of the management, and if necessary appropriate penalties should be meted out to combat the spoilage and prevent carelessness.

The production planning department will only issue instructions to replace rejects or losses (Table 14.11) if material has to be allocated to fulfil the programme. If the component stock level is maintained and the rejects or losses do not interrupt the functioning of the plant, the spoilage is replaced in the next planning period. The instructions are approved by the chief engineer or deputy director of the plant in the presence of a representative from the shop (the superintendent or his

Table 14.10 (*Continued*)

| | | | | | | | LS-59-1, round bar | | | | | | | |
|---|---|---|---|---|---|---|---|---|---|---|---|---|---|---|
| 22 | 25 | 28 | 30 | 32 | 36 | 40 | 45 | 50 | 55 | 70 | 75 | 80 | 90 | 100 |
| 1060 | 2357 | 1711 | 3304 | 24 | 2047 | 770 | 608 | 157 | 300 | 313 | 67 | 163 | 387 | 280 |
| 380 | 457 | 633 | 1172 | 6 | 1525 | 620 | 360 | 157 | 228 | 99 | 67 | 124 | 342 | 280 |
| 379 | 1113 | 684 | 1212 | 18 | 250 | 98 | 225 | — | 72 | 137 | — | 39 | 45 | — |
| 301 | 787 | 394 | 920 | — | 272 | 52 | 23 | — | — | 77 | — | — | — | — |
| 1088 | 3163 | 1834 | 3406 | — | 2304 | 841 | 877 | 175 | 420 | 504 | — | 405 | 498 | 522 |
| 881 | 2009 | 1148 | 2289 | 30 | 2945 | 716 | 870 | 292 | 434 | 349 | 105 | 360 | 761 | 709 |

deputy) guilty of the spoilage. The material is supplied within a day or two of his approval by the following procedure.

The rough-component shop material planning section calculates the material requirement from the instruction and forwards a requisition for unplanned supplies to the supply department. The number of the instruction and date of approval are also indicated in the requisition. The supply department enters the additional requirement in the overall supply plan (see Table 14.11) in the 'Amended requirement' column. The rough-component shop planning-control office makes out the material order for every item in the instruction, gets it approved by the head of the supply department and organizes the issue of the materials to production.

The stores will issue material over and above the limit on receipt of a signal order from the supply department.

Increasing attention is being paid in materials planning to the question of amendments to the production plan. Whenever the need arises for a substantial cut in the production schedule or a major increase in output for a planning period, the head of the production planning department has to agree to the draft of the change in plan with the deputy commercial director. The agreed draft is approved by the director of the plant. This procedure for altering the production plan enables the commercial staff to take timely steps to fulfil additional or rescheduled targets.

Experience in the adoption of group technology and the organization of group production indicates that close attention must be paid to the

Table 14.11

Approved:
Chief Engineer

### INSTRUCTIONS TO REPLACE SCRAP

To the Manager, Shop No. 5.
You are to take from stock and produce the following components to replace spoilage:

| Item | O/No. | Product symbol | Component No. | No. off | Deadline | Authority No. and date |
|------|-------|----------------|---------------|---------|----------|------------------------|
| 1 | 05321 | BR–1 | 4 | 112 | 15/III | 461, 11/III |
| 2 | 05321 | BR–1 | 25 | 85 | 15/III | 464, 12/III |
| 3 | 04318 | IM–7 | 48 | 32 | 20/III | 365, 11/III |
| 4 | 04248 | BI–8 | 62 | 15 | 15/III | 367, 11/III |

provision of supplies. The deputy head of the PPS must devote most of his working time to keeping the shops supplied with materials and blanks.

The plant central expediting office must have a progress clerk controlling the materials supply situation. Every large machine shop should have a technician in charge of materials supplies.

Deputy commercial directors are recommended to convene shop materials supplies meetings once or twice a week; it would be as well to allocate specific days of the week for this purpose. All this will require attention, time and effort; but the cost is steadily recouped by the smooth production flow and freedom from troubles engendered by lack of materials.

# 15

# the function of the chief designer's and chief production engineer's departments in group production conditions

IT HAS been stressed over and over again that the successful adoption of group techniques depends on every department in a commercial enterprise, and in this respect the performance of the chief production engineer's and chief designer's departments will obviously play a major part. To begin with, the staffs of these departments must have more or less equivalent qualifications. The chief production engineer's qualifications, persistence and initiative should match those of the chief designer. The prestige of the chief production engineer's staff should be high, and it is absolutely essential that staff in the chief designer's department should take notice of their views. This must be said because at some plants the chief designer's department operates under more privileged conditions, and the differentials — which still exist — in salaries do not always permit managements to secure a balance of qualifications between these departments.

Under group production conditions, when the problem is faced and solved of raising the number of components machined by group techniques to at least 80 per cent and at the same time greatly simplifying the preparations for new production processes and cutting the time taken in drawing up the production sequences and designing the tooling, it is the chief production engineer's job to furnish the chief designer with his requirements regarding the practicality of the designs. In collaboration with the standardization and normalization department he must adhere strictly to the established procedure for keeping the plant functioning smoothly.

It must be said frankly that when enterprises start to operate on group principles major differences of opinion arise between the chief

H

production engineer's and chief designer's departments, which require the daily intervention of the chief engineer or plant director. Lack of co-ordination between these two key departments in a plant can upset its entire course of operation on group principles.

When the chief production engineer's department has issued catalogues of components already in production that are covered by group technology and with the help of the works management persuaded the designers to use them, the organization of the work on group principles is made much easier.

Table 15.1 PROGRESS IN THE ADOPTION OF GROUP
TECHNOLOGY FOR NEW PRODUCTS

| Standard products | | New products | |
|---|---|---|---|
| Symbol | Percentage conversion to group technology | Symbol | Percentage conversion to group technology |
| — | — | MIN–8 | 81 |
| — | — | MBI–9 | 83 |
| MBI–1 | 69 | MBR–1 | 95 |
| MBI–3 | 61 | MBR–3 | 94 |
| MBI–4 | 63 | MBD–1 | 91 |
| — | — | AU–26 | 89 |

Table 15.1 gives the actual progress made in adopting group technology for a number of items already in production and a number of new items at an Association plant.

The contribution of the chief designer's department can be seen from the data given. The number of basic production components in the new products, though they differ a great deal from the basic products and in some cases have nothing at all in common with them, is very high. This is success indeed and represents the contribution of the basic production designers to the development of group technology, which should be encouraged and maintained in every way possible.

The extensive use of components already in production in new products has reduced the volume of production documentation and released production engineers and designers for other work. The graph in Fig. 15.1 shows how documentation has been reduced as a result of transferring the components to group technology. During the five years the enterprise has been in operation the production documentation has been nearly halved, although the skill ratings of the production engineer planners have fallen sharply. On the other hand the skill ratings of the production engineers setting up the production groups, should, as experience has shown, be exceptionally high. The head of the group technology office should have a status equal to that of the main shop superintendents and enjoy the same rights as the deputy chief production engineer.

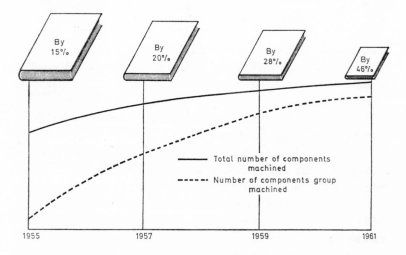

*Fig. 15.1* Graph showing the reduction in technical documentation

The introduction of group techniques is closely linked with the extended use of group attachments. Plant managers must instruct chief production engineers to cut down on single-component attachments and, using special schedules, personally fix deadlines by which new group attachment designs are to be introduced. In view of the fact that group attachments are usually easier to design and make than special purpose tooling, as more components are transferred to group machining the proportion of tooling can thus be raised without increased labour costs.

The statistics in Table 15.2 show how the proportion of tooling for new production processes goes up with the number of standardized

Table 15.2 INCREASE IN THE PROPORTION OF TOOLING
AFTER MODIFICATION AND CONVERSION TO
GROUP TECHNOLOGY

| Instrument symbols Before    After modification | Year of intro- duction | Percentage of unified compts | Percentage of group technology | Tooling units Total    For group use | Proportion of tooling |
|---|---|---|---|---|---|---|
| MBI-3    — | 1955 | 12 | 48 | 180 | 53 | 1.9 |
| —    MBR-3 | 1960 | 28 | 94 | 197 | 177 | 2.7 |
| MBI-4    — | 1954 | 9 | 29 | 187 | 85 | 2.1 |
| —    MBD-1 | 1960 | 32 | 91 | 285 | 190 | 3.2 |

components and components produced by group techniques. With a higher proportion of tooling, it is possible to employ less highly skilled machine operators; the labour productivity is increased and the product quality improved.

The chief production engineer's department must prepare the change-over to group machining techniques in accordance with a carefully drawn up plan adapted to the specific production conditions.

Only when the staff of an enterprise have overcome all of the difficulties involved in converting the components to group technology on one type of equipment, drawn up the documents, worked out the methods of planning and organizing the workplaces and so on, can a start be made on converting components to group technology for other operations. Fig. 15.2 shows how new group machining sequences have been assimilated year by year within the Association.

The group technology office must be expanded by reinforcing the design and production engineering staff with highly skilled workers, preferably long-serving engineering and technical personnel from the shops. It is recommended that financial incentives be offered to all of those taking part in work to do with group technology. The possibilities should be explored as far as possible within the scope offered by the specific operating conditions at the enterprise concerned. Fig. 15.3 shows how the group technology office has expanded at one of the Association plants.

The chief production engineer's department must maintain liaison with the rate-fixing and standardization department, since the unification of components plays a big part in group production and in some cases can radically influence the production techniques to be used.

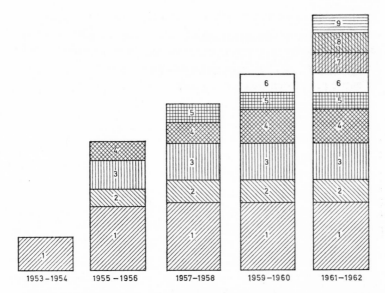

*Fig. 15.2* Graph showing the increasing assimilation of different group production operations

1 – capstans; 2 – drilling machines; 3 – milling machines; 4 – pressure diecasting; 5 – liquid-metal stamping; 6 – finishing; 7 – centre lathes; 8 – woodworking; 9 – tool production

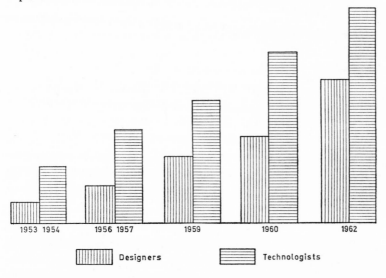

*Fig. 15.3* Graph of the organization of production preparation in connection with the introduction of group technology

If the chief designer's and chief production engineer's departments and also the rate-fixing and standardization department are producing good work, and are properly organized and purposeful in their approach, the chances are that the entire plant will function well. The success of the entire production function depends on these three departments.

# 16

# the cost effectivness of
# group production

AN EXAMINATION of the results of applying group techniques to the machining of components indicates that a change in the basis of production sequences to group principles provides enterprises with the following major economic benefits.

1 The labour productivity of the workers is increased as a result of the reduction in working time per unit of output and the consequent saving on wages.
2 Expenditure on service personnel salaries is reduced as a result of the reduction in the number of setters, job allocators, foremen and others.
3 The cost of making special tooling (attachments and dies) is reduced as a result of the replacement of single-component with group tooling.
4 The costs of planning the production sequences and designing the tooling are reduced.

Table 16.1 gives details of the cost reductions on the design and manufacture of attachments achieved on changing over to group machining.

The following actual results have been obtained by the Association and represent typical examples of the economic benefits to be derived from changing over to group machining methods. One plant has recorded savings by adopting pressure diecasting in group dies for medium- and small-batch components, formerly made as sand castings.

Table 16.1 COST REDUCTIONS ON THE DESIGN AND
MANUFACTURE OF ATTACHMENTS ON ADOPTING
GROUP TECHNOLOGY

| Tooling | Cost reduction (%) | |
| | Design | Manufacture |
| --- | --- | --- |
| Lathe attachments | 68.5 | 59.0 |
| Milling fixtures | 42.0 | 66.0 |
| Drilling jigs | 51.5 | 63.5 |
| Pressure diecasting dies | 58.0 | 69.0 |

1 On materials 15–25 per cent of the weight of the castings, as a result of the reduced machining allowances.

2 On wages 12–20 per cent in the machine-shop and 5–10 per cent in the foundry;

3 As a result of the lower cost per tonne of pressure diecastings compared with sand castings.

The total saving on the production costs per tonne of rough diecast components amounts to 25–28 per cent of the cost of the equivalent components produced as sand castings.

Enterprises introducing group machining on capstan lathes show major savings. Experience has shown that in the first two years of operating capstan lathes on group machining principles the Optico-Mechanical Association achieved the following encouraging results.

1 Time spent in tooling up and resetting the lathes has been cut to 30–35 per cent of time taken when they were operated on individual sequences.

2 Component labour costs have fallen on average by 25–35 per cent with the result that the labour productivity of the operators has risen by 33–50 per cent.

3 The number of machine setters has been halved.

4 The number of work allocations and foremen has been reduced as a result of the reorganization of planning and servicing.

5 Expenditure on tools and attachments has fallen by 30–40 per cent.

The total annual saving per capstan lathe operating on two shifts is

2–2·5 thousand roubles, while the costs of changing a capstan section over to group production sequences do not exceed 200 roubles per machine, which includes modifying the equipment, organizing the workplaces and training the operators in group machining techniques.

Similar results are achieved on converting other types of equipment to group machining techniques.

The substantial reduction in the time spent on the technical preparations for production represents perhaps the most significant economic benefit to be derived from changing over to group machining. Thus, the time the production engineers spend on planning the production sequences is reduced by 15–20 per cent, and the drawing office labour costs on the design of special tooling for single components are reduced as follows: 60–70 per cent for turning work, 50–60 per cent for milling, 60–70 per cent for pressure diecasting and 90–95 per cent for machining on automation. The times taken to prepare the technical documentation and make the tooling are reduced accordingly, and this of course is of enormous help in organizing a smooth production flow.

These cost effectiveness examples indicate that major economic benefits can be derived from the use of group sequences. The cost of introducing them is not particularly large and their use represents a progressive means of substantially improving the technical, economic and production performance figures within enterprises.

# 17

# the preparation of a plant
# for changing over to
# group technology

A GREAT deal of preparatory work is needed to convert an entire plant to group production techniques. The style and methods of work in the supply, production planning, chief designer's and chief production engineer's departments must be changed. Only if these departments are functioning efficiently can group techniques be introduced throughout the plant.

The problem of keeping the various shops supplied with materials and blanks is always an important one at any plant, but on the adoption of group production techniques it assumes especial significance, since stoppages and interruptions in the flow necessitate resetting machines to handle components not in the groups scheduled for them.

To ensure that the machine shops are being supplied with materials and blanks, intake schedules are drawn up for these materials, with a certain anticipation allowance, and a strict watch is kept to see that they are adhered to. At the progress meetings held every 10 days with the plant director, the deputy director reports on the materials supply situation in the machine shops and appropriate steps are taken to eliminate any holdups in supplies.

The deputy commercial director holds weekly progress meetings to discuss the supply of materials and equipment, to which he invites all of the shop and section heads concerned. Material substitution problems are tackled at these meetings with the assistance of the chief designer's department, the technical control section and a representative of the client, if the substitution is a result of a breakdown of supplies.

Schedules are arranged at the progress meetings and steps taken to safeguard them. The production planning department dispatcher has the job of seeing that they are adhered to.

Supplying the shops with components and co-operative deliveries is the responsibility of the co-operation department. If no such department exists a small independent office should be set up, for experience has proved that the provision of a co-operative department can substantially improve the operational efficiency.

Much of the work involved in organizing group production falls on the production planning department. The methods of planning to specified dates and the planning of supplies to keep every machine fully occupied acquire especial significance with group technology. Planning in the face of the so-called backlog which exists, unfortunately, in every plant however large or small plays a very big part. For this purpose it is recommended that a production organization office with a staff of three to five, depending on the size of the plant, be set up in the production planning department. A skilled worker, ideally one of the heads of the shop planning central offices, should be recommended for the post of head of the production organization office. The cost of setting up such an office is quickly recouped against the smaller number of service personnel required in the shops.

The office must be given the task of drawing up the detailed job schedules for the month, quarter and year related to the component batch sizes and the labour costs, but with the proviso that each machine is kept fully occupied with a group of components. The production organization office is also responsible, together with the chief production engineer's, labour and wages and supply departments, for preparing the entire planning documentation and seeing that it is introduced into the plant shops.

Extensive reorganization is necessary in the chief production engineer's department, where the entire effort must be geared to the adoption of group techniques.

Much attention must be given to manning the group technology office with skilled workers, and here the shop superintendent can render valuable assistance. Knowing the tremendous benefit that the plant can derive from the adoption of group techniques, they should assign skilled workers from their shops to the office. Thus a group technology office with a staff of 15–20 specializing in every type of work, from machining

Table 17.1   'GROUP TECHNOLOGY' SECTION
(Extract from the works plan for organizational and technical measures—ORGTEKHPLAN)

| Description of measure | No. of components | Stages of completion | Departments responsible* |
|---|---|---|---|
| 1 | 2 | 3 | 4 |
| 1. Introduce the group machining in machine shop No. 3 of components transferred from other shops (to be made on capstans, millers and drilling machines) | 600 | Select items<br>Draw up sequence and design tooling<br>Make tooling<br>Master the technique<br>Adopt in production | DO & PEO<br><br>PEO<br>Toolroom & foundry<br>PEO & machine shop No. 3<br>PPS, machine shop No. 3 |
| 2. Convert lathes in machine shop No. 6 to group machining | 1500 | Select items<br>Draw up sequence and design tooling<br>Making tooling<br>Master technique<br><br>Adopt in production | PEO & DO<br><br>PEO<br>Toolroom<br>PEO & machine shop No. 6<br>Machine shop No. 6 |
| 3. Adopt group technology on capstans in machine shop No. 6 | 450 | Select items<br>Sequence and tooling<br>Make tooling<br>Master<br><br>Adopt | PEO & DO<br><br>PEO<br>Toolroom<br>PEO, machine shop No. 6<br>Machine shop No. 6 |
| 4. Adopt group technology on millers (8 in number) in machine shop No. 9 | 300 | Select items<br>Sequence and tooling<br>Make tooling<br>Master<br><br>Adopt | DO & PEO<br><br>PEO<br>Toolroom & foundry<br>PEO, machine shop No. 9<br>Machine shop No. 9 |
| 5. Adopt group technology on turret autos in machine shop No. 3 | 400 | Select items<br>Sequence and tooling<br>Make tooling<br>Master<br><br>Adopt | DO & PEO<br><br>PEO<br>Toolroom<br>PEO, machine shop No. 3<br>Machine shop No. 3 |

*Abbreviations: DO—Chief Designer's Department (Drawing Office)
PEO—Chief Production Engineer's Department
(Production Engineering Office)

Table 17.1 (*Continued*)

| J | F | M | A | M | J | J | A | S | O | N | D | Source of finance | Estimated cost (th. rb.) | Purpose of measure | Estimated annual savings (th. rb.) |
|---|---|---|---|---|---|---|---|---|---|---|---|---|---|---|---|
| 5 | 6 | 7 | 8 | 9 | 10 | 11 | 12 | 13 | 14 | 15 | 16 | 17 | 18 | 19 | 20 |
| 30 | 30 | 50 | 60 | 60 | 70 | 70 | 70 | 80 | 80 | | | Shop running costs | 3.3 | Increase labour productivity by reducing aux. time | 6.0 |
| | 30 | 30 | 50 | 60 | 60 | 70 | 70 | 70 | 80 | 80 | | | | | |
| | | 45 | 50 | 65 | 60 | 65 | 70 | 70 | 75 | 80 | 20 | | | | |
| | | 30 | 40 | 60 | 60 | 70 | 70 | 70 | 75 | 75 | 50 | | | | |
| | | 20 | 30 | 60 | 60 | 60 | 70 | 70 | 70 | 70 | 90 | | | | |
| 150 | 150 | 150 | 150 | 150 | 150 | 200 | 200 | 200 | | | | Shop running costs | 9.0 | Increase labour productivity by reducing aux. time | 16.8 |
| | 150 | 150 | 150 | 150 | 150 | 150 | 200 | 200 | 200 | | | | | | |
| | | 150 | 150 | 150 | 150 | 150 | 150 | 200 | 200 | 200 | | | | | |
| | | 100 | 100 | 150 | 150 | 150 | 200 | 200 | 200 | 200 | 200 | | | | |
| 100 | 100 | 100 | 100 | 150 | 150 | 150 | 200 | 200 | 200 | 200 | 200 | | | | |
| 100 | 100 | 100 | 100 | 50 | | | | | | | | Shop running costs | 1.2 | Increase labour productivity by reducing aux. time | 1.9 |
| | 50 | 50 | 100 | 100 | 100 | 50 | | | | | | | | | |
| | | 50 | 50 | 100 | 100 | 100 | 50 | | | | | | | | |
| | | | 50 | 50 | 100 | 100 | 100 | 50 | | | | | | | |
| | | | | 50 | 50 | 100 | 100 | 100 | 50 | | | | | | |
| 50 | 50 | 50 | 50 | 50 | 50 | | | | | | | Shop running costs | 6.5 | Increase labour productivity and improve planning | 6.5 |
| | 50 | 50 | 50 | 50 | 50 | 50 | | | | | | | | | |
| | | 50 | 50 | 50 | 50 | 50 | 50 | | | | | | | | |
| | | | 50 | 50 | 50 | 50 | 50 | 50 | | | | | | | |
| | | | | 50 | 50 | 50 | 50 | 50 | 50 | | | | | | |
| | | 50 | 50 | 100 | 100 | 100 | | | | | | Shop running costs | 6.0 | Increase labour productivity and improve planning | 1.0 |
| | | | 50 | 100 | 50 | 100 | 100 | 100 | | | | | | | |
| | | | | 100 | 100 | 100 | 100 | | | | | | | | |
| | | | | | | | 100 | 100 | 100 | 100 | | | | | |
| | | | | | | | 100 | 100 | 100 | 100 | 100 | | | | |

Table 17.1 (*Continued*)

| Description of measure | No. of components | Stages of completion | Departments responsible* |
|---|---|---|---|
| 1 | 2 | 3 | 4 |
| 6. Adopt group technology for drilling operations, using 4- and 6-position drilling heads | 8 heads | Select items<br>Design heads<br>Make heads<br><br>Master<br><br>Adopt | DO & PEO spread<br>PEO<br>Toolroom<br><br>PEO, machine shop No. 1<br>Machine shop No. 1 |
| 7. Adopt group die blocks for small-batch pressure diecastings in No. 2 shop | 45 items | Develop tools and technique<br>Make dies<br>Master<br>Adopt | PEO<br><br>Toolroom<br>PEO & shop No. 2<br>No. 2 shop |
| 8. Adopt group fixtures in finishing sections (electro-static paint spraying) | 100 | Develop technique (groups)<br>Design fixtures<br>Make fixtures<br>Master<br>Adopt | PEO<br><br>PEO<br>Maintenance shop |
| 9. Convert electroplating section in shop No. 7 to group technology | 10000 | Group items<br>Develop plating conditions<br>Design fixtures<br>Make and test fixtures<br>Adopt | PEO<br>Works lab.<br><br>PEO<br>Maintenance shop<br><br>PEO, No. 7 shop |
| 10. Adopt group technology in case manufacture in No. 14 woodworking shop | 110 | Select items<br>Sequence<br>Design tooling<br>Make tooling<br><br>Master<br>Adopt | PEO, DO & shop 14<br>PEO & shop 14<br>PEO & shop 14<br>Toolroom & maintenance<br>PEO & shop 14<br>No. 14 shop |

*Abbreviations: DO—Chief Designer's Department  (Drawing Office)
PEO—Chief Production Engineer's Department
(Production Engineering Office)

| Deadline dates (January–December) | | | | | | | | | | | | Source of finance | Estimated cost (th. rb.) | Purpose of measure | Estimated annual savings (th. rb.) |
|---|---|---|---|---|---|---|---|---|---|---|---|---|---|---|---|
| J | F | M | A | M | J | J | A | S | O | N | D | | | | |
| 5 | 6 | 7 | 8 | 9 | 10 | 11 | 12 | 13 | 14 | 15 | 16 | 17 | 18 | 19 | 20 |

spread over the entire year — Shop running costs — 1.2 — Increase labour productivity by reducing aux. time — ▬

2  3  3

Special funds — Adopt die-casting for new products — ▬

5  5  5  10  10  10
10  10  10  15
10  10  10  15
10  10  10  15

Shop running costs — Increase labour productivity and reduce tooling costs — ▬

Shop running costs — Increase labour productivity and reduce technical design time — ▬

Shop running costs — 1.0 — Increase labour productivity and reduce design and tooling costs — ▬

and finishing to final assembly, can be set up by using the shop personnel.

At the same time it is useful to transfer an engineer to the post of deputy shop superintendent in one of the key shops fitted out with every type of equipment and making the most important components with skilled labour. This man will have worked in the chief production engineer's department on the establishment of group technology. The promotion of key personnel in this manner should reap major benefits.

With a view to achieving greater flexibility in the adoption of various attachments designed on group principles, it is recommended that a workshop fitted out with a comprehensive range of equipment be set up within the chief production engineer's department. The various types of group attachment can then be made in the workshop, where they can be carefully examined by the staff of the chief production engineer's department before they are handed over to the shops.

The operation of the chief production engineer's department and toolroom must be very strictly regulated in matters of the design and manufacture of group attachments. Indeed, what sense is there in making single-component attachments for new products or doubling up on existing attachments, when they can be replaced by group attachments?

The tasks of designing and making the group attachments must be strictly controlled and no delays must be tolerated in their completion to schedule. In the event of the toolroom failing to turn out its quota of group attachments the plan cannot be regarded as having been satisfactorily fulfilled and a penalty factor should be introduced. If on the other hand the workers fulfil their tasks ahead of schedule they should be suitably rewarded.

Every shop should be given monthly group technology tasks, and their fulfilment must be treated as part of the fulfilment of the basic plant programme.

The chief production engineer must report on the progress made in the adoption of group technology at the progress meetings held every 10 days with the plant director.

A special 'Group technology' section (Table 17.1) has been included in the organizational and technical measures plan at the Association plants since 1961.

# 18

# the role of the trade unions and the party organizations in the assimilation of group production techniques

THE TRADE unions and the Party organizations within the plant, which are called upon to maintain or help put into practice anything new or advanced, obviously have a major part to play in the adoption of group machining methods.

Every innovation causes difficulties, even if it only concerns a small section of work. Group production involves reorganizing the efforts of the entire plant staff and cannot be solved by administrative measures alone. One should not be surprised if the rhythm of production is disturbed for a short period when group techniques are first adopted.

The likely reason for this is that when the groupings are arranged the components already behind schedule are not distributed evenly among all of the groups and their production will consequently be delayed still further in the assimilation period. Under these circumstances such components must not be handed out haphazardly for production on all of the machine tools, otherwise all of the tooling arrangements for all of the groups of components will be upset.

Experience has shown that cases occur when 'unprofitable' components are included in the group for one machine, thereby upsetting the operator and sometimes inciting him to resist the adoption of group production methods. The shop management must take immediate steps in conjunction with the trade union and the party organizations to tackle such problems, turning if necessary for assistance to the plant labour and wages department. Members of the trade union and the party organizations can, by taking control of the introduction of the first group sequences, be of considerable help to the shop managers in

I

giving top priority to the supply of materials and blanks to the group technology section.

The trade union and the party organizations and plant management also have much to do during the period when the section and later the shop are being fitted out with the necessary cutting, gauging and auxiliary tools. It is recommended that joint consultations be held during this period between the toolroom and machine-shop Party offices, at which problems connected with the group technology tooling arrangements can be discussed.

The discussion of group production problems at the plant Party Committee meeting is of tremendous benefit, because the Committee members and the executives in charge are particularly well aware that group production methods must be introduced at the plant.

The plant newspaper and radio broadcasts are of considerable importance. The progress in the adoption of group technology must be systematically spotlighted and the good and bad points noted. The newspaper published by the Leningrad Optico-Mechanical Association can serve as an example in this case. It has kept its readers up to date on the progress made in introducing group machining methods by means of brief weekly notes. When the group technology machine section had been operating for a year on group principles it published a jubilee issue, in which the workers wrote:

'I must confess that I was a reluctant convert to the group machining approach. It seemed to me that there was nothing to gain from it, I should not learn how to mind my machine without assistance and my wage packet would not benefit. But if it were suggested to me now that I transfer to another machine operating under the old system, I should object. I should object because in this section I have learnt so much that is new.'

Capstan operator N.Ya. Romanovskaya.

Capstan operator V. N. Kravchuk wrote:

'The time has long since passed when group technology capstan operators expressed unwillingness to employ the new system. Now everyone who works in this section is content and takes pride in its achievement.'

The fact that the capstan operators rapidly mastered this new method, gained satisfaction from their job, began to earn more and increased their skill ratings is largely due to the foremen and team leaders, who with the backing of the management and Society organizations worked purposefully with tremendous eagerness and interest.'

Capstan operator E. E. Burkanova wrote on this subject:

'To master the work on the capstan lathe one needed persistence and guts. In the course of each shift, team leader Kostrova came up to my machine time and again to explain and demonstrate how to set the machine, sharpen the tool and set it up. Now the team leader seldom comes up to me because she knows that I need less help than I used to.'

One can see even from these brief notes that the adoption of group techniques encounters difficulties until the employees realize the benefits that it will bring to the plant and themselves.

An interesting case occurred at one of the Association plants. Workers of the chief engineer's department and machine shop displayed a very commendable initiative. On examining a group of massive components comprising some 50 items machined in individual sequences, the production engineers and shop foremen decided that if certain design modifications were made some of the components could be combined in a new production group, while the remainder could be made on existing group sequences. It must be said that this proposal was received without much enthusiasm by the design staff. Then the trade union and the party organizations stepped into the breach. The production engineer's suggestion was discussed at a joint meeting in the Party offices between the chief production engineer's and chief designer's departments. The plant newspaper devoted an issue to the proposal, recording the views of the workers, foremen, production engineers and managers of the shops and departments.

The machine-shop superintendent, S. P. Mironov, wrote in his article, 'A way of further extending the group machining approach', as follows:

'We considered that the work of establishing group machining techniques in a small-batch plant with a large range of components should begin at the design stage. The designer should take into account and lay the foundations that permit the use of the group machining method. However, this was not the case and we were perfectly justified in our decision to submit the design of the components concerned to a critical appraisal.

'It should not be impossible to find ways and means of grouping the components by simplifying their design without of course impairing their overall quality.'

The deputy superintendent of the foundry, L. I. Reshetnikov, wrote:

'Certain changes in the design of these components will do more than simplify the machining by making them an easier proposition for production as sand castings. Component No. 163 for example need not incorporate a cavity, the core for which used to account for 20 per cent of the moulding time.'

The senior machine-shop foreman, I. V. Veprintsev, had this to say:

'The adoption of the design modifications has reduced the labour costs in the finishing shop as well as the foundry and machine shop. Furthermore, several components can now be made as pressure die-castings.'

The designer, K. V. Nikolaev, expressed the following thought:

'I was confronted with the task of redesigning the components to reduce the machining labour costs without impairing the quality of the product. The results have demonstrated that of the eight modified components four can be passed at once for production and will give a 25–30 per cent reduction on labour costs. Several dozen of these components have already been sent to assembly.'

The Association has issued an order, referring to the commendable initiative displayed by the group of workers who set the stage for the

adoption of group machining techniques by making the design modifications and improving the technological features. The instigators of the
effort were thanked officially and a team was set up to complete their
work.

The resulting conversion of this large group of massive components to
group production techniques has produced a saving of 35 000 roubles
per annum.

The production engineering and design staff are continuing to
collaborate but the initiative is now coming from the chief designer, who
is making provision in the drawings of new components for the possibi-
lity of machining them in group sequences.

# 19

# the development of
# group technology

THE GROUP approach is being applied ever more widely to the manufacture of machinery and instruments in the Soviet Union. The Party and government are giving great encouragement to the development of this method. The June (1959) Plenary Sessions of the Party Central Committee designated group technology as one of the main directions of technical progress in engineering.

Group machining methods have now been adopted at more than 100 enterprises in Leningrad, producing goods in small and large batches. More than 500 000 components have been group machined.

Group technology has become an integral part of the plans for the development of new techniques in most of the engineering and instrument-making plants in the Leningrad economic district.

The group production committee of the Technical and Economic Council of the Leningrad Council of the National Economy (C.N.E.) has played an important part in popularizing the new method. It includes scientists, organizers and production engineers, all enthusiastic advocates of this progressive technology.

The first All-Union Conference of enterprise and research institute workers was held in November 1959 at Leningrad to propagate and systematize the practical experience gained by industry in the use of group production sequences in engineering and instrument-making. The Conference was convened by the State Committee for the Co-ordination of Research in the R.S.F.S.R.,* the Leningrad C.N.E. and the Scientific-Technical Societies of the engineering and instrument-making industries. More than a thousand experts from 104 centres throughout the Soviet Union attended the Conference.

* Russian Soviet Federative Socialist Republic.

The Conference made the following recommendations with a view to developing group technology and modernizing and automating equipment.

1 Review the existing production setups at small- and medium-batch plants, giving the change-over to group production top priority in the production planning.

2 Extend the work of classifying the items produced in every shop on a basis of the design and operations required for specific manufacturing processes (machining on capstan and centre lathes, drop forging, casting, plastics moulding, etc.), a necessary preliminary- to the large-scale planning of group production sequences.

3 Ensure that the designs of products to be made using group methods are technologically quite suitable. It is essential that design staff and production engineers should collaborate from the outset on the design and production of new items.

4 Increase the effort on the unification and standardization of components and their elements.

5 Adopt group machining techniques not only on individual operations, but throughout the entire component-manufacturing cycle on a basis of similarities in the operations required and the batch repetition frequency.

6 Combine the development of group technology with the modification of existing equipment to provide maximum mechanization and automation of the production sequences.

7 Extend the use of multi-product flowlines with quick-change, standardized tooling and high-productivity automated equipment based on the use of pneumatics, hydraulics, electronics and the unit design principle.

The Leningrad C.N.E. has passed a resolution calling for the wide-scale adoption of group production techniques. Special offices have been set up in many plants and their design and production engineering staffs are engaged in designing and developing the attachments and technology for group production. The C.N.E. Boards drew up a plan for the development of group technology, under which the following pieces of equipment were to be converted for group machining: 7918 in 1963, 9900 in 1964, and 11450 in 1965.

This plan is being successfully implemented at Leningrad plants. In 1962 there were 119 group flowlines in operation at engineering concerns in the city. Group flowlines and sections have been successfully introduced at the Kirovsk, 'Elektrosila', 'Reduktor', 'Kotlyakova' and many other plants. Group flowlines have been set up at the 'Poligrafmash' plant to deal with levers, brackets and other flat components.

Number 3 shop at the Izhora plant has gone over entirely to operation on group principles. Twice the output is now obtained on the same equipment and same floorspace. Group production techniques are also being used in the foundries at the Neva 'V.I. Lenin', 'Vulkan' and 'S.M. Kirov' PTO plants, and the group machining approach has been adopted in furniture-making at the 'Khalturin', 'Lunacharskii' and other foundries.

The Leningrad Production Engineering Research and Design Institute (NIITMASh) is doing a tremendous job. In 1962 it gave help in introducing production methods to 55 national economic councils throughout the Soviet Union, including the Gorkii, Kiev, Novosibirsk, Georgia and Chelyabinsk.

With a view to extending the use of the new method, the State Committee for the Co-ordination of Research in the R.S.F.S.R. organized an All-Union seminar in conjunction with the Leningrad C.N.E. Production engineers, foremen and machine setters representing some 200 plants studied group production techniques for a month at plants in Leningrad. They received technical instruction, including operating the machines on their own, and are now pressing ahead with the adoption of group machining techniques at enterprises in their own economic regions.

Group machining is now being used at more than 15 plants in the Volgo-Vyatsk economic region. High proportions of the components made at the biggest concerns in the Central Urals economic regions, such as Uralmashzavod and the turbine-engine works, are group machined.

At the Ryazan Heavy Forge and Press Equipment plant the components for every item produced have been classified, with the result that some 70 per cent of the components are now machined in group standard production sequences.

The Mogilev 'Strommashina' plant has introduced the group approach to cold-forming operations, so that die-design labour costs have been cut by 70 per cent and the time spent in making dies by two-thirds.

A great deal has been done at the Kiev 'Arsenal' works. Nearly all of the capstan lathes and index-type automatics have been converted for group machining, as also have a large number of millers on which the components are machined in group attachments. The centre lathes have also been modernized for group machining.

Leningrad scientists and engineers have been of great help in introducing group production methods in the German Democratic Republic, the Czechoslovak Socialist Republic and other socialist democracies. A team of experts led by V. M. Gerts, the head of the Leningrad C.N.E. Central Office of Technical Information, has rendered invaluable assistance to Czechoslovak industry in the adoption of group production techniques. The fact that most Soviet literature on group production has been translated into the Czech indicates the intense interest in this method.

Experts from East German commercial enterprises have studied group production methods at Leningrad plants. The Lenin prize-winner Doctor of Technical Sciences S. P. Mitrofanov, Doctor of Technical Sciences A. A. Matalin and others have given lectures in East Germany.

The new technology has received approval at the Harbin and Tientsin Polytechnic Institutes. Chinese engineers declare in a letter to Leningrad engineers:

'Acquaintance with the technical literature of other countries (the United States, Japan, United Kingdom, Sweden, etc.) on engineering and instrument manufacture indicates that the Soviet Union was definitely the first to develop group machining, and the method itself is likely to be extensively utilized in many countries as one of the most progressive methods for the scientific and practical manufacture of machines and instruments.'

Obsolete machinery and instruments must be replaced if products are to meet the present-day requirements of science and technology. The frequent modifications entail massive and costly production planning.

Accordingly group technology affords the opportunity of cutting the cost and time of tooling-up for new production.

The resolutions of the 22nd Congress and November 1962 Plenary Session of the Party Central Committee make great demands of workers in industry regarding the future development of new advanced production techniques, including group production.

Plant managements, scientific workers, engineers, technicians and foremen must help in designing the attachments and introducing group techniques. If everyone plays his part success will be guaranteed!

# index

Accuracy, 16, 17
Aluminium alloys, 46, 52, 73
Anodizing, 50, 52
Assembly, 12, 48, 52, 53, 116; operations listed and coded, 54; sequence, 53, 55
Attachments, 2, 3, 8, 12, 18, 21, 27, 28–9, 34, 48, 49, 50, 52, 57, 61, 63, 71, 103, 108, 116; catalogues of, 58; classification of, 58; for centre lathe, 60; for milling machines, 73; inserts in, 56, 57, 58, 60, 71, 73; setting-up of, 71; term defined, 27
Automatic transfer equipment, 52
Automatics, 1, 5, 12, 125
Automation, 109, 123
Avoidance of bypassing (on capstan lathes), 34

Backlog, 111
Basic component, 9
Basic consumption rates, 89, 94
Batch-production plants, 12
Batch sizes, 1, 2, 12, 14, 16, 17, 111; increasing, 15
Blank-forming techniques, 38, 42
Blanks, 42, 45, 77, 110; rationalization of, 38; stocks of, 87
Blowholes, 43
Body components, 5
Brass, 27, 73
Bush-type components, 5, 22, 23, 62

Capstan lathes, 1, 5, 9, 10, 12, 15, 16, 17, 18, 19, 20, 21, 26, 27, 32, 33, 34, 36, 37, 63, 65, 66, 69, 70, 73, 108, 109, 119, 123, 125; automatic operating cycle, 65; programme controlled, 64, 66, facing 69
Capstan operators, 36, 118, 119
Capstan setter, 33, 36
Carry-over stocks, 94, 98
Catalogues, 19, 24, 55, 58, 102
Centre lathes, 5, 8, 12, 13, 14, 16, 17, 21, 22, 37, 57, 60, 62, 73, 123, 125; additional slides on, 62; attachment for, 60; programme controlled, 64, 66, 68; rational use of, 21
Chief designer's department, 101, 102, 106, 110, 119; co-ordination with chief production engineer, 102
Chief production engineer's department, 70, 73, 89, 101, 102, 103, 106, 110, 111, 116, 119
Chromium plating, attachment for, 50, 51
Clamping arrangements, 57, 71
Clamping attachment, quick-acting, 34
Classification of components, 3, 4–7, 26, 41, 46, 123, 124; scheme of, 4
Classification system, 52, 58
Closed production cycle principle, 67
Coefficient of proportionality, 84
Cold extrusion, 38
Cold-forming operations, 125
Collet chuck, 20; group, 34–5
Complicated components, 19–20, 24
Component deficits, 75
Component groups, 7, 11, 13, 17, 19, 21, 26, 46, 50, 62, 87
Components: manufacture, 12; modification, 104
Component production sequence, 3

Component programme, 92
Composite objective, 53
Composite part, the, 8 *et seq.*
Composite product, 52
Conference on Group Production, Leningrad, November 1959, 122; recommendations of, 123
Continuous milling, 71; attachment for, 71–3
Controller, 65
Conveyors, 12
Co-operation department, 111
Copper alloys, 46
Copy slide, 36, facing 20; hydraulic, 62, facing 68, 63
Cost effectiveness, 107, 109
Counterweight, 58
Cross slide, 65; power operation, 66
Cutting tools, 61
Cyclogram, 50
Czechoslovakia, 125

Data-processing section, 78, 81, 95
Deputy shop superintendent, 116
Design and operations, 5, 6
Design classification, 24, 39
Design modifications, 120
Design section, 13
Design staff, 119, 121; essential to collaborate with production engineers, 123
Die block, *see* Group die block
Diecasting, *see* Pressure diecasting
Dimensional accuracy, 19, 20, 22, 27, 42, 64; of diecastings, 39
Dispatcher, 111
Drawings, 17
Drilling machines, 5, 57, 73
Duralumin, 27

Ejector system (diecasting), 39, 40, 41, 46
Electrical equipment, 67
Electronic computers, 68
Electroplating, 48, 49
Electrostatic spray painting, 48
Engineering plants, 69, 73
Equipment loading plan, 78, 80, 81, 82
Extra drive, 65, 66

Feedback sensors, 65
Financial incentives, 104

Finish machining, 23
Finishing operation, eliminating, 36
Finishing processes, 48, 49, 116
Fitting, 52; *see also* Assembly
Flat components, 24
Flowlines, 12; multi-product, 123
Friction presses, 45

Gating system, 39, 40, 41; central gating, 40
Geometric shape of components, 5, 9
'German Democratic Republic', 125
Government, 122
Grinding machines, 5, 12
Group approach, 3, 56
Group chuck, 20, 58, facing 52
Group die blocks, 39, 40, 41, 42, facing 21, facing 52, 46; savings from, 42, 107; water cooling for, 46
Group fixture, 24, 25
Group flowlines, 2, 124
Group machining, 2, 10, 14, 18, 24, 25, 32, 33, 36, 56, 62, 76, 104, 108, 109, 118, 119, 121, 122, 123, 124, 125; advantages of, 2; assimilation of, 105; basic concept of, 2; savings from, 37, 107, 108, 109
Group milling attachment, 59, facing 53
Group production; conditions, 75, 101; problems, 118
Group production sequences, 3, 4, 7, 8, 9, 17, 19, 26, 27, 33, 34, 49, 50, 52, 53, 57, 63, 69, 70, 75, 77, 78, 79, 80, 81, 86, 107, 109, 119, 121, 122, 123
Group setting, 18, 19
Group setup, 10, 32, 49
Group techniques, 18, 50, 67, 101, 103, 104, 107; changeover to, 36, 37, 70, 110, 112–15; 123; difficulties of adoption, 75, 117, 119; economic benefits of, 107, 119
Group technology, 33, 37, 42, 46, 69, 83, 102, 122; development of, 122; equipment, 78; monthly tasks, 116; outlined, 1 seq., popularizing, 122; progress in adopting, 102; savings from, 14, 37, 108
Group technology office, 70, 78, 103, 111
Group technology shop, 69–74, 112; organization of, 111–15; performance of, 73–4

Group turning sequences, examples, 22–3
Grouping, 4, 5, 11
Groups, 2, 17, 41

High productivity equipment, 1, 2, 12, 13, 123
Horizontal heads, 19
Hydraulic copy slides, 62, facing 68, 63
Hydraulic presses, 45

Ingate, 40, 44
Innovation, difficulties of, 117
Instructions card, 27, 30, 31
Instructions for finishing, 49
Instrument making, 69, 73
Intake schedules, 110
Interchangeable inserts in dies, 39, 41, 42, facing 21, facing 52, 46
Investment casting, 38

Jigs, 58, facing 53, 59, facing 68; plates, 59
Jig designers, 33
Job cards, 2, 52, 57, 89, 90
Jobbing production, 13, 21
Joint consultation, 118

Keys, 25

Labour costs, 111
Labour productivity, 12, 13, 16, 21, 23, 36, 50, 56, 64, 69, 70, 73, 74, 104, 107, 108
Lathes, 57; *see also* entries listed by individual type
Lead times, 89
Liquid-metal stamping, 20, 38, 42, 47; basic concept, 42; compared with diecasting, 42; cost saving, 45; demand on dies, 45; material costs, 46; metal-pouring setups, 43; replaces drop-forging, 42, 45; with extrusion, 44; without extrusion, 44, 45
Lists: of attachments, 27, 28–9; of components, 26, 27; of operations, 54
Loading schedules, 76, 77, 78, 80, 82

Machine-shop, 118
Machine tool loadings, 17, 24, 36, 67, 81; estimating, 76; schedule of distribution, 76
Machine tool specialization, 62
Machining allowances, 38, 39
Machining costs, 14, 74
Machining cycle, 68
Machining sequence, 9, 16, 64
Machining time, 33, 61
Magnetic contact principle, 50
Maintenance, 67
Management, 69, 118
Mass production, 12, 39, 52
Material consumption, 91
Material estimates, 88
Material planning, 89; section, 88, 95, 99; system, 88
Material stocks, 91, 98
Material supplies, 87–100, 110, 118; daily returns, 98; estimating stocks of, 88, 91; issued, 97; plan, 96, 97, 98, 99; schedule, 89, 92; time for, 87
Materials list, 89, 92
Materials requirements, 89, 92, 96; for internal consumption, 97
Materials substitution, 110
Mechanization, 12, 13, 18, 21, 49, 123
Metal utilization, proportion, 38
Microscope objectives, assembly of, 53, 54, 55
Microswitches, 65
Milling, 109
Milling cutter, 24, 71
Milling machines, 5, 12, 23, 24, 35, 57, 69, 70, 71, 73, 125; bench, 70; group attachments, 73; horizontal, 24, 70; multi-position attachments for, 58; requirements for group production, 71; universal, 70; vertical, 25, 70
Milling-time nomogram, 86
Modification of machine tools, 61, 62, 65, 69; cost of, 66
Multi-position machine stop, 36, 62
Multi-tool slides, 62

Nomograms, 85; for milling times, 85, 86
Non-ferrous alloys, 42, 45
Norm overfulfilment factor, 77

One-off production, 12
Operating programme for capstan lathe, 64
Operating schedules, 77, 78, 81, 82

Operation-by-operation interpolation, 84
Operational programme, 77, 82
Output increase, 36, 74
Output targets, 77

Painting and varnishing, 48, 49
Parting line, 39, 40, 41
Party organization, 69–70, 117, 118, 119, 122
Piece time, basic, 83
Planning and record card, 92, 93, 94, 95
Planning documentation, 111
Planning period, 89
Planning targets, 94; amendments to, 99
Plant newspaper, 118, 119
Plant production plan, 77
Plating baths, 48, 49
Pneumatic clamping system, 62, 71
Pneumatic drives, 64
Pneumatic-hydraulic drives, 64
Preparatory work, 7, 56, 76, 105, 109, 110
Preset programme, 52
Pressure diecastings, 20, 38, 39, 42, 107, 108, 109, 120; machines, 40, 43
Product sets, 88; defined, 88
Production costs, lowering of, 38
Production documentation, 1, 2, 49, 52, 104, 109; reduction of, 50, 102, 103
Production engineer, 1, 8, 33, 48, 68, 94, 95, 103, 119, 121, 123; mechanizing work of, 68; qualifications, 101; skill rating, 103
Production engineering section, 13
Production organization and planning, 1, 3, 13, 17, 37, 48, 68, 69, 73, 75, 76, 105, 112–15
Production planning section (PPS), 78, 81, 89, 92, 98, 110, 111
Production schedules, 87, 88; amendments to, 99
Production sequences, 1, 3, 4, 5, 8, 12, 13, 18, 21, 48, 49, 53, 62, 88; planning basis, 15, 16
Productivity of machines, 34
Programme control, 64–8; difficulties of 67; numerical, 68; preparation of programmes, 68
Programme instructions, 68

Programmed machine tools, 67
Progress meetings, 110
Punched cards, 66, 96

Radio broadcasts (in plant), 118
Rapid setting-up techniques, 61
Rate fixing: card, example, 84–5; department, 104, 106; group approach to, 85, 86; methods, 83, 84; simplificaton of, 50; technically based, 83, 85, 86
Rear slides, 62
Representative component, 83, 84, 85
Resetting of machine tools, 12, 18, 33, 36, 70, 76, 110; times, 15, 21, 61, 108
Retooling, 16
Rhythm of operation, 66
Rouble, new, 42
Rough components, 9, 12, 17, 77, 88, 89, 90, 91, 94, 95, 96, 99
Roughing operations, 18, 22

Salary differentials, 101
Scrap: reduction of, 36; replacement of, 100
Shaft-type components, 5, 22
Shell moulding, 38
Silumin, 27
Simple components, 19
Slotted components, 24
Slotting attachments for capstan lathes, 19, 35, facing 20, 36
Small batch production, 12, 13, 14, 16, 17, 18, 21, 34, 39, 42, 45, 48, 52, 56, 63, 64, 69, 70, 83, 107, 120
Special fixtures, 23
Special profile tools, 34
Speeds and feeds, changing automatically, 66
Spoilage, 98, 99
Staff, 104
Standard component, 62
Standard stocks, 87
Standard times, 50
Standardization, 45, 55, 123
Standardization and normalization department, 101, 104, 106
Steel, 27
Stepped components, 62
Stepping selectors, 52, 65
Stock levels, 87, 94, 98
Stocktaking, 94, 95

Supplies department, 73, 88, 91, 97, 98, 99, 110, 111
Supply failures, 75
Supply problems, 87
Supply system, 88
Surface finish, 16, 17, 19, 20, 27, 42; of diecastings, 39
Swarf: reducing amount of, 38; removal, 57, 58

Template, 63
Thread-cutting attachment, 9, 19, 26, 36
Tolerances, 22, 57
Tooling, 2, 6, 7, 9, 12, 33, 55, 56, 69, 101, 103, 104, 107, 109; costs, 56; permanent, 33; stocks, 58; time, 14, 17, 108
Toolrooms, 70, 116, 118
Trade unions, 69, 117, 118, 119
Transfer line for anodizing, 50
Turning, 109

Turret heads, 21, 23
Turret lathes, 13, 14

Unification, 55
Universal attachments, 21, 70
Universal lathe, 20
Unit head machine tools, 2, 57, 63, 69; for shaped slots and surfaces, 63, facing 69
'Unprofitable' components, 117

Vertical heads, 19, 34, 36

Woodworking, 48
Work cabinets, 36
Work in progress, 87, 95
Work volumes, 81
Workers' opinions, 118–20
Working documents, 26, 27, 49, 52
Working parts, simplifying, 62
Workplace organization, 36, 104
Workshop, 116